PIONEERS OF THE HIGHLAND TRACKS

WILLIAM AND MURDOCH PATERSON

A Biography of Two Railway Engineers

Anne-Mary Paterson

The Highland Railway Society
November 2010

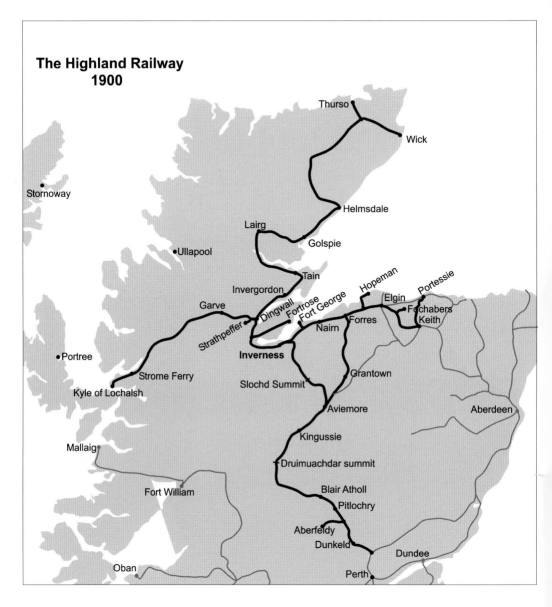

The Highland Railway
1900

© Anne-Mary Paterson 2010
ISBN: 978 0 95454855 1

Front cover : Murdoch Paterson's masterpiece, the Nairn Viaduct at Culloden, as photographed by Ewan Weatherspoon from the east on a frosty morning.

Cover design by Vicky Wharton, Pencil Ltd.

Published by the Highland Railway Society : www.hrsoc.org.uk.

Printed by Information Press, Eynsham, Oxfordshire, OX29 4JB

CONTENTS

This book is dedicated to my husband, Iain, without whose encouragement I would never have completed the book, and to my father, the late William Paterson, from whom I inherited my interest in railways and civil engineering.

Anne-Mary Paterson is a great grandniece of William and Murdoch. She is an honours graduate of the Open University. She is interested in local history, especially in the Beauly area where she now lives with her husband.

Acknowledgements

Many people have assisted me with this project. I would especially like to thank the Highland Railway Society for publishing this book and in particular Keith Fenwick for his hard work editing and putting together the book. Neil Sinclair has spent a lot of time giving me very useful advice and information including reading through my manuscript twice. Caroline Hutton and Howard Geddes read through the text and made many useful amendments. David Ross read the manuscript and gave me helpful hints. I am also indebted to the assistance given to me by Michael Chrimes, Librarian at the Institution of Civil Engineers.

I wish to thank Vicky Wharton for designing the cover of this book, Hamish Roberts for allowing me to use his grandfather's photographs now given to the Highland Railway Society, Olivia Brotheridge for providing the illustration of Murdoch on the Culloden Viaduct, Iain Marr for allowing us to reproduce the picture "The Old Stone Bridge," Hilda Hesling for providing photographs, Linlithgow Union Canal Society, Canon Black of St Michael's and All Angels, Inverness, for information on my Episcopalian relations, Mr and Mrs Ross, Fearn, for their hospitality and allowing me to view John Ross' diary, Jane Anderson, Archivist at Blair Castle, the owners of Achanor Bed & Breakfast and of the former stationmaster's house at Culloden for allowing me to photograph their houses, the committee of the Inverness Field Club for allowing me to use photographs from their transactions taken during the construction of the Culloden Viaduct, Richard Casserley for permission to use his father's photographs, the staff of the reference library and the genealogy department in Inverness and Dingwall Libraries, and the staff of the Highland Council Archives, in particular their retired archivist Bob Steward, who looked out useful documents for me.

These days one needs to acknowledge the information obtained from the Internet sites Scotland's People and Find My Past. Without them I would have had to spend many hours looking through paper or microfiche records in Edinburgh and London.

My thanks to all others who may have helped and are not mentioned.

FOREWORD

When reviewing significant historical engineering works to be included in *Civil Engineering Heritage Scotland, 2007,* no less than seven outstanding works of Murdoch Paterson from c.1860 to 1898 came to my notice. These were the Findhorn viaduct; Allt-na-Slanach timber viaduct (modified in 2001); Culloden Moor or Clava viaduct; Waterloo bridge, Inverness; Oykell viaduct, Invershin; Wick bridge; and Wick railway station. Remarkably, all are still in service and the viaducts are magnificent structures in the finest Highland tradition of Telford (1757-1834) and his dedicated assistant, of *Reminiscences of my Life in the Highlands* fame, Joseph Mitchell (1803-1883).

Civil engineering is about directing the great forces in nature for the use and convenience of mankind. In the second half of the 19th century this is nowhere better exemplified in the Highlands than in the works of Mitchell and the Patersons. Their connection with Telford's practice was by no means tenuous, both having been apprenticed to chief assistants of the great engineer, and also as partners of Mitchell. Mitchell was the driving force in implementing and extending Telford's Highland road and harbour improvements and, after his death, in developing the railway network from Perth northwards to Wick by 1874. From 1875 to 1898, as Engineer to the Highland Railway, Murdoch Paterson's work can be considered to have brought railway coverage in the Central and Northern Highlands more or less to its zenith.

The author Anne-Mary Paterson deserves great credit for taking on the challenging task of writing this book. I feel sure that she will not mind my revealing that her interest in civil engineering arose from having as a father another William Paterson who was also a civil engineer in the railway industry. His last project before retirement involved electrification of the Glasgow Suburban lines in the late 1950s and 1960s. Anne-Mary considered taking up a civil engineering career herself but, in the 1950s when she left school, this was not generally considered a proper occupation for women and there were hardly any in the profession. It is therefore particularly fitting that her early interest has blossomed into this fascinating portrayal of two largely unsung heroes who contributed so much to Scotland's transport infrastructure.

Roland A Paxton

Professor Roland Paxton MBE FICE FRSE
School of the Built Environment Heriot-Watt University
Vice-chairman ICE Panel for Historical Engineering Works

Descendants of Donald Paterson Standard Bearer at Culloden

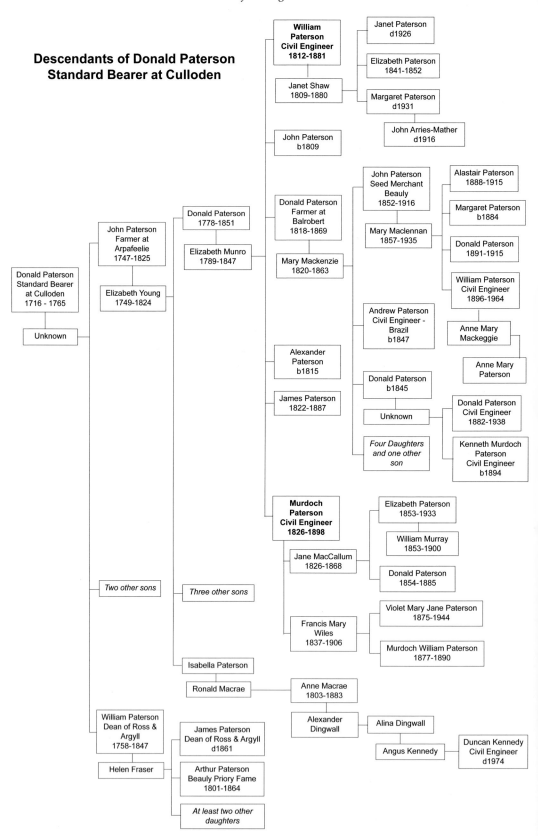

PROLOGUE

It was an autumn day over twenty years ago. I was sitting in a window overlooking a square in Edinburgh's new town with a second cousin. He had asked me to help him to sort out the contents of a box of family papers. We found it contained papers of William Paterson, a civil engineer, my great granduncle and the Shaw family into which he married. I took away all the papers that interested me and so began my enquiries into William and his youngest brother, Murdoch. I knew quite a bit already from my father and my aunt about Murdoch and his career building railways radiating from Inverness. However, I was curious to know more about William and how he and Murdoch came to take up the profession of civil engineering, something entirely different from their forefathers. And so began my exploration of my Paterson forebears. It was to take me along a road of many new surprises.

Legend has it that in the 15th and 16th centuries Sir William and Sir Thomas Paterson, who were churchmen, owned land at Dores and Culcabock, near Inverness. The family probably migrated from somewhere in Scandinavia to become traders in the Black Isle and Inverness areas in northern Scotland. Their descendants were extravagant with their money but one John Paterson (c.1604–1679) became Episcopal Bishop of Ross. His son, also John, became Bishop of Edinburgh and then the last Episcopal Archbishop of Glasgow in 1687, just before the Presbyterian Church became the established church in Scotland in 1690.

Like many in Ross-shire and other parts of the Highlands, the family clung on to the Episcopalian worship after 1689 when William and Mary came to the British throne. Many Episcopalians who felt they could only swear allegiance to a Stuart monarch were ardent Jacobites. Probably for financial reasons and because of their political leanings the family returned to the North Kessock area of the Black Isle across the firth from Inverness. They were tacksmen. A tacksman was a person, probably peculiar to the Highland clan system, who leased a large piece of land called a tack from the local laird, which he then leased to sub-tenants. In return he would sometimes do favours for the laird such as training his foot soldiers and assisting when he went to war with other clans.

Donald Paterson, the person at the top of our family tree, was born about 1716. He was also a Jacobite and a tacksman. We do not know when he took up arms with Prince Charles Edward Stuart in the 1745 uprising or if he went on the ill-fated march to Derby. Family tradition claims he was a standard-bearer in the Jacobite army at the Battle of Culloden in 1746, perhaps even a standard-bearer to the Prince himself. In the confusion after the Jacobite defeat, he escaped and made his way back to North Kessock. The Duke of Cumberland sent his troops to search the countryside far and wide for Jacobite fugitives. Donald's position was becoming more and more untenable. He considered fleeing on a ship berthed in Inverness that was bound for Holland. However, he reckoned without his redoubtable wife who had other ideas, as she could not bear the thought of long years of separation if he was captured.

There were sticks in the farmyard that she arranged so that she could hide her husband inside the pile. There he stayed for six weeks. Every day, at great risk to herself, she took food and water out to him in the hours of darkness. The Duke of Cumberland issued a proclamation denouncing death by hanging for every person who harboured an insurgent. Anybody who concealed arms or ammunition would have a similar fate. Proclamations read out in towns demanded the surrender of

William Paterson.   *(Anne-Mary Paterson collection)*

arms, information on rebels and knowledge as to the whereabouts of the Prince. The General Assembly of the Church of Scotland praised the Duke and requested that clergy in every parish read out notices on similar lines. Roman Catholics and Episcopalians were to have an even worse fate. The only way for rebels to escape death was to take an oath of allegiance to the Hanoverian King George II.

Donald and his wife were in a quandary. Someone might notice that he was missing and report this to the authorities. What should they do? They decided with a heavy heart that there was only one thing to be done and that was to go to Inverness and take the oath. Whether he actually took the oath is debatable but he certainly surrendered the blade of his sword as today his descendants are left with just the hilt – a precious relic from the battle. There are two other swords in the family's possession, one is English and the other Dutch, presumably looted from the battlefield, so Donald left his options open for another day by concealing these weapons.

Donald had four sons, Andrew, Alexander, John, my four times great grandfather, and William, his youngest, born in 1758. William went to Marischal College, Aberdeen and was ordained into the Episcopal Church in 1780. He became incumbent of Arpafeelie and other parishes in the Black Isle from 1784 to 1827 and then Dean of Ross and Argyll from 1837 to 1841. He was a small man, so nicknamed "The Little Parson." Archdeacon Craven in his *Journal of Bishop Forbes* described him as "a neat, tidy little man." Apparently, he was very fastidious in his habits and this gave the impression of being a dandy.

Dean William married Helen Fraser who came from Lettoch near Beauly. She too was an ardent Episcopalian with Jacobite leanings. They had two sons, James and Arthur, and several daughters, described as tall and stately when they grew up.

The Dean died aged 89 in 1847. His grave is within the walls of Beauly Priory, by this time a ruin. Before the Reformation it was a priory of the Valliscaulian Order from Burgandy. John Bisset, a forbear of the Frasers of Lovat, founded it in 1230. William's wife's family had burial rites there. James, his older son, also went into the Church and became rector of Arpafeelie and then of St John's Ballachulish. He then became Dean of Argyll and the Isles from 1846 to 1848.

The Scottish Episcopal Church of the twenty-first century is in full communion with the Church of England but in the late eighteenth and early nineteenth century services were very simple and often in Gaelic in the Black Isle. James Boswell on his tour of Scotland with Samuel Johnston in the early 1770s wrote of a church in Inverness "The altar was a bare fir table, with a coarse stool for kneeling on ......". Services with hymns were just starting. There were no candles or ornamentation. Communion was infrequent. The congregation received communion tokens prior to the celebration as in the Presbyterian Church in those days.

John, Dean William's brother and my forebear, attended Arpafeelie church with his family. The present church, St John's built around 1816, is signposted off the new A9 north of Inverness and the Kessock Bridge. The following incident would have taken place in the older church that was adjacent. As the Sundays passed, John was becoming increasingly annoyed because William always waited for the laird, presumably Mackenzie of Allangrange, to arrive. He and his family were persistently late. In those days William would have been dependent on the laird for his stipend so he would not wish to displease him. This was not good enough for John who told his brother that if he waited one more Sunday for the laird he would leave the church. The next Sunday came. William waited for the laird. Just as the clattering of hoofs heralded the laird's arrival, John, accompanied by his wife and a string of

Murdoch Paterson, in later life.
(Highland Railway Society/Roberts Collection)

children marched, out of the church. The next Sunday, much to the amazement of the congregation, he arrived with all his family at the Church of Scotland. It was highly embarrassing for all concerned because John was the farmer at Arpafeelie. For nearly three generations there was no contact between the families.

Dean William had another son, Arthur, and a number of daughters. Arthur was a great disappointment to his father, who had hoped he would go into the Church like his brother James. In 1845, it seems he was living in Beauly and his occupation, if any, is unknown. A funeral party arriving at the priory found the gates locked. This was because the Lord Lovat of the day had decided that the priory and the churchyard should be for his exclusive use. Arthur was furious because this meant his family would lose the right of burial. He was a large man and, leading a band of villagers, he broke down the gates with a big hammer and then the door to the priory itself, allowing the mourners to enter with the coffin. Since then the Lovats have used Eskadale in Strathglass as their burial ground.

There is no mention on the tombstone of Helen, Dean William's wife, or of Arthur. His son James, who died in Fortrose, is buried there.

John, Dean William's brother, had five surviving children including Donald, my great great grandfather, who was a farmer at Dell of Inshes near Inverness. William and Murdoch Paterson were two of his sons.

Kyle of Lochalsh on the opening day, 2nd November 1897.

(Highland Railway Society collection)

THE BEGINNINGS

On a November day in 1897, against many odds, the very first train steamed into Kyle of Lochalsh station. The Highland Railway had reached its furthermost point on the west coast of Scotland. It was a day of triumph for all concerned. The platform was crowded. Photographers were busy recording every detail.

And so it was that this famous railway line, one of the great train journeys of the world, was born. This journey is not only an experience of wonderful scenic beauty but also one that traverses some of the most difficult terrain for a railway in Britain. In spite of this, the Victorian engineers and workers completed their job on what was at that time to be one of the most expensive railway lines in Britain.

Murdoch Paterson, my great granduncle, was the civil engineer who designed and masterminded its construction. Though a single-minded man he was, according to accounts, very kind. He was able to get the best out of anyone who worked for him. Above all, he was the person who carried on the flame of Joseph Mitchell, the master railway builder of the Highlands, and of Thomas Telford, civil engineer *extraordinaire*.

How did it all come about? Murdoch, born in 1826, was the youngest of seven children, six boys and one girl, Elizabeth. Like many other families in those times seven other children died in infancy. Their father, Donald, was the tenant farmer at Dell of Inshes, Inverness. The Patersons were said to have an unusually good relationship with their landlord, the Robertsons of Inshes. The farm was in the country in those days, not swallowed up by the expanding city of Inverness as it is now. All up the east coast of Scotland there is a band of fertile soil and the Paterson farm was situated on this.

Their mother was also Elizabeth. The oldest son was John and then came William, born in 1812. The family, by the terms of those days, seem to have been fairly well to do. During the Napoleonic Wars, agricultural prices remained high so no doubt the more industrious of farmers made good money. The whisky industry was expanding as well, so there was a demand for barley. Oats were also a staple crop in those days.

William was three when his next brother, Alexander, came along. Then came Donald, my great grandfather, Elizabeth, James and youngest of all Murdoch. They went to school, including Elizabeth, and must have received a good education, particularly in mathematics judging by the future professions of William, Alexander and Murdoch. Elizabeth won prizes at Inverness Royal Academy. In those days, many parents considered it was not necessary to educate girls, especially if it cost them money, so it is a reflection of their parents' modern ideas.

The Highlands were still in turmoil after the defeat of the Jacobite army led by Charles Edward Stuart at the Battle of Culloden in 1746. Communication was difficult as there were no proper roads except those constructed for military use by General Wade between 1725 and 1733, and then in the 1750s by Major Caulfield. By 1786, when the British Fisheries Society was formed, these roads were in bad condition. In 1796, the government appointed Thomas Telford as its surveyor and the Treasury instructed him to look into the establishment of fishing stations and the construction of a canal from the east coast to the west coast of Scotland.

Between 1801 and 1803, Telford made a number of recommendations to Parliament, including the establishment of the Highland Roads and Bridges Commission. The counties covered were Inverness,

Ross, Sutherland and Argyll. By 1821 the commissioners had completed one thousand one hundred and sixty six miles of road, including the improvement of two hundred and eighty miles of military roads. They had overseen the construction of one thousand one hundred and seventeen large and small bridges. The roads were usually ten or twelve feet wide, built of a six to twelve inch layer of local gravel or stones bound together. All had proper culverts and drains.

During the Napoleonic Wars, the government needed better communications especially for shipping and moving personnel around. It was thought that a canal through the Great Glen from Inverness to Banavie near Fort William would assist shipping going between the east and west coasts, save time and avoid the perilous Pentland Firth between Orkney and mainland Scotland. Construction of the Caledonian Canal, also designed by Thomas Telford, started in 1804. Like many projects, it turned out that the canal was not finished by the time of the defeat of the French at the Battle of Waterloo in 1815.

The Highland landowners were looking for ways to make their estates more profitable. Those who had supported the Jacobite cause had their lands taken over by the government after the defeat at Culloden. By the early nineteenth century, the authorities had returned most estates. One improvement that the landowners liked was to turn their land over to Black Face sheep. This involved removing their tenant crofters from many of the glens and settling them on the coast. Some of the displaced emigrated to America, Australia and New Zealand. Maybe those left who were able bodied and in need of work found it as labourers on the canal.

These problems may have had little effect on life on a farm near Inverness. During the Napoleonic Wars because of restricted imports of grain and the necessity of feeding a bigger army, prices increased and many improvements took place in agriculture. With the end of the war in 1815, the price of commodities slumped but barley still fetched a good price because of the increase in the number of whisky distilleries.

It must have been a busy household with farm and home duties. William and Murdoch's mother Elizabeth was probably pregnant a lot of the time and no doubt the children had to lend a hand on the farm, as work was much more labour intensive than nowadays. The cattle and sheep needed feeding, the cows milking, the poultry tending and the fields cultivating. No doubt in many ways the farm was self-sufficient. Besides the farmhouse, there would be a bothy where the servants lived. There was always a ploughman as ploughing went on when the weather was suitable from October to March so that the fields were ready for sowing. He was also in charge of the horses, usually Clydesdales, that pulled the ploughs and other farm machinery. There would also be servants in the house to do cooking, washing and ironing and housework

However, six sons could not continue on the farm so they needed to look for other jobs. Two, Donald and James, did follow their father into farming, James on Dell of Inshes and two other farms and Donald at Balrobert, near Inverness.

Inverness in the early nineteenth century was not much bigger than what we think of now as a large village. It grew up around the river and the harbour as shipping was its most important method of communication. Church Street, which runs from the castle to the Old High Church, is one of the oldest streets. Houses grew around centres such as the harbour and the river crossings.

Inverness Royal Academy, which the children attended, was founded in 1792 in New Street, now Academy Street; this runs parallel to Church Street. It replaced the Old Grammar or Latin School that was in Dunbar's Hospital in Church Street. Teaching was in English. The present day school holds in its archives the book of prizewinners, and subjects taught included Mathematics, Natural Philosophy, Geography, Latin and Greek, English and History. William did not win any prizes but his younger brother, Alexander, gained a number including one for good general attention and in 1840 a silver medal for mathematics.

Winter days are short in the Highlands. They would have done their school homework by candle light. At weekends, there would be jobs on the farm as well. Clydesdale horses were the tractors of those days. There would be other horses to ride and pull the dogcarts and other conveyances. This is probably how the children went to school each day and the whole family to Church on Sundays as it would be too far to walk to the town.

When William was born the Caledonian Canal had been under construction for nine years. The Eastern section to Loch Ness opened in 1818. At Clachnaharry where the canal starts, then a separate village from Inverness, the embankments leading to the sea lock thrust out four hundred yards over the mud banks of the Beauly Firth. The entire length to Banavie opened in 1822 though work continued until the 1840s. A major engineering project like this was probably a great source of interest to curious small boys. Although it was some distance from their home the canal was not too far to walk from Inverness Academy.

About a mile from Clachnaharry is Muirtown Basin, much nearer Inverness. A flight of four locks raises the canal thirty-two feet. They are still a great attraction when the gates and the swing bridge carrying the road across the canal opens to allow shipping to pass.

No doubt, William had heard stories of the building of the Bell Rock lighthouse by Robert Stevenson and his further exploits with lighthouses around the coast of Scotland. When William was about eighteen years old, the first main line railway, between Manchester and Liverpool, opened. Maybe he was fired by these tales, so decided to follow a completely different occupation from the rest of the family, that of the very new profession of civil engineering.

The term "civil engineer" was first used in the late eighteenth century. The Egyptians, the Greeks, and the Romans all designed and constructed projects such as the Pyramids, aqueducts, and irrigation schemes. John Smeaton was the first person to call himself a civil engineer in a report on the Forth & Clyde Navigation, as opposed to a military engineer like General Wade, constructor of military roads in Scotland. This was during the age of canals. Smeaton and some other civil engineers founded the Society of Civil Engineers in 1771.

Telford was a busy man designing and supervising the construction of many projects throughout Britain from harbours, churches, manses and canals in Scotland and Sweden to bridges such as that over the Menai Straits to Anglesey. He appointed trusted employees to supervise his work. Telford's first choice of John Duncombe to look after the building and maintenance of the roads and bridges in the Highlands turned out to be unfortunate. Duncombe died mysteriously in prison in Inverness after five years in the job. He had worked for Telford on the Ellesmere Canal but he seems to have been carried in the new job by his two assistants, one of whom was John Mitchell, a

A boat leaves the lock at Clachnaharry on the Caledonian Canal on its way from Muirtown basin to the Moray Firth. The embankments which extend the canal into the Firth as far as the sea lock can be seen beyond the boat. This was a sight which William must have seen in his childhood.

(Keith Fenwick)

stonemason from Forres who had worked on the Caledonian Canal at Fort Augustus. Telford noticed him as a competent and trustworthy man. On Duncombe's death, he appointed John Mitchell as chief inspector. Mitchell had assistants in each county but nevertheless he travelled up to nine thousand miles each year on horseback, in carts and carriages or on foot in all weathers, sleeping in damp huts and inns in order to inspect the various jobs in hand.

John Mitchell's career with the Highland Roads and Bridges Commission lasted until his death in 1824 aged forty-five. His son Joseph, one of his seven children, succeeded him. John thought that experience as a stonemason would be a good start for Joseph's chosen career as a road builder, so he sent him to work on the Caledonian Canal at the western end. During this time Joseph used to practice his draughtsmanship skills so Telford asked him to construct a panoramic view of the Caledonian Canal. Telford was so impressed with the young lad's work that he invited him to London for training in 1821. Telford had just gone to live at 24 Abingdon Street in Westminster. Joseph became involved with many of Telford's jobs at that time. As well as civil engineering colleagues, Telford had many other friends like the poet Robert Southey, whom young Joseph probably met. As well as learning the job he was acquiring other skills such as speaking to people older and wiser than himself.

News came in July 1824 that John Mitchell was dangerously ill so Joseph returned north to Inverness. John died in September. Joseph had carried out all his father's tasks so efficiently during his illness that six months later at the age of twenty-one Telford appointed him to succeed his father. Many thought that he was far too young to undertake such a job.

William Paterson, a curious small boy on a visit after school, may well have spoken to John or Joseph or even the great Thomas Telford himself on one of his visits to Scotland.

William probably left school about 1829 or 1830 when he was seventeen or eighteen. There is no record of what he did then though one can surmise that he worked for Joseph Mitchell. There were terrific floods in August 1829 that caused landslides and damage to many bridges including Telford's famous bridge at Craigellachie. Repairs took until 1831 so Joseph may well have employed extra staff to help with the work.

News of the Liverpool and Manchester Railway would have appeared in the newspapers and excited many people though it was to be nearly a quarter of a century before the people of Inverness saw a train.

Sometime later in the 1830s William set off to work in Ireland. Ireland's very first railway ran from Dublin to Kingstown, now Dun Laoghaire, where a new harbour was established as the river Liffey at Dublin itself was too shallow for the larger draught ships introduced in the nineteenth century.

We can only guess at William's journey. Maybe he went to Fort William via the Caledonian Canal, then by sea to Glasgow, or by stagecoach to Glasgow and then on to Belfast by sea. In any case it would not be a quick journey.

William would never have seen a real train and, of course, there were no photographs in those days. Maybe there were drawings in newspapers but his chosen career was very different from his upbringing on a farm near Inverness. However he came to make this choice of learning about railway engineering, it was a good one. At that time John Macneill, later Sir John, was surveying possible routes for railways in Ireland. He too had been an assistant of Thomas Telford so would be known to Joseph Mitchell. He is reputed to have been an excellent teacher and in 1842, Trinity College, Dublin appointed him as their first professor of the Practice of Engineering.

Railway engineering was still in its infancy. At this time, there was no set gauge for railway tracks. The Dublin to Kingstown, the first railway in Ireland, was of four feet eight and a half inches, what is nowadays the standard gauge, although some Irish railways decided on six feet two inches. The rails, made of iron from Dowlais Ironworks near Merthyr Tydfil in Wales, sat on longitudinal sleepers of American pine with cross sleepers every ten or fifteen feet. The railway was single track.

William's time in Ireland would have been very valuable training for his future work in the Scottish Highlands, which had no railways.

Prior to his work in Ireland, John Macneill was involved in the design of the Slamannan Railway, which was given Royal Assent in July 1835. William transferred to this railway after his period in Ireland, presumably to gain experience in the construction of a line. The Slamannan in central Scotland was part of a system not originally intended for passenger use but for carrying freight to canals. The first railway of this group was the Monkland & Kirkintilloch which opened in 1826 to carry goods, especially coal, to the Forth & Clyde Canal from the Monkland Canal and used horse power. The Monkland Canal, twelve miles long, carried coal from the North Lanarkshire mines to Glasgow, a city growing with the wealth of the tobacco merchants.

The Ballochney Railway opened in 1828 as an extension to the east from the Monkland & Kirkintilloch. The Slamannan ran from Airdriehill on the Ballochney Railway to Causewayend on the Union Canal which starts at Edinburgh. This canal joined the Forth and Clyde Canal near Falkirk through a series of locks. Passage through the locks was slow and tedious so using the railway and then the canal would be a quicker route to Edinburgh for coal and other goods. In the twenty-first century, the Falkirk Wheel, a revolutionary Millennium project, joins the two canals, bypassing the series of locks.

At first these railways were envisaged to transport coal to Edinburgh. The main industry of the area including Slamannan was coal mining. Horses rather than steam engines were used to pull the wagons. At Causewayend a basin was formed in the canal for transferring the cargoes of coal to the canal barges. The rails surrounding the basin and the seating for the cranes are still visible today.

This coal was to rival shipments to Edinburgh from the Fife coalfields, dispatched by sea out of Charlestown on the north side of the Firth of Forth. However, by the time the railway opened, ideas had changed. Steam engines were used and for a brief period passengers were carried while travelling between Glasgow and Edinburgh, first by train and then on the Union Canal. This ceased on the opening of the direct line from Glasgow to Edinburgh in February 1842.

The Slammanan Railway was single track but if there was sufficient traffic to make it profitable, there was enough room to make it double track. It was twelve and a half miles long and built to a gauge of four foot six inches. The

Causewayend Basin as it is today. The upper photo shows the remains of the base for a crane.   *(Linlithgow Union Canal Society)*

Slammanan Church where William & Janet Shaw were married. It is now a private house.   *(Anne-Mary Paterson)*

rails lay on longitudinal lengths of pine resting on cross sleepers. Part of the railway was over peat moss. Someone reported that the track, which in effect was floating over the bog, sank two to three feet with the weight of the train passing over it and then returned to its correct level. The first part of the railway climbed out of Airdrie, crossed a plain via Slamannan and then dropped steeply again to Causewayend at a gradient of one in twenty-two for eight hundred yards. A stationary engine at the top of the inclined plane assisted the trains up and down the slope.

Thomas Telford Mitchell, a brother of Joseph, was engineer in charge. His appointment was in the summer of 1836 so William arrived during the construction period. Sir John, being a good teacher, was probably giving him experience of the next stage in railway building after surveying, that of actually constructing the line.

But affairs of the heart were to intervene. Charles Shaw of Dalquhairn was a small landowner near Avonbridge, a village between Slamannan and Causewayend. The Shaws had owned considerable land around Dalquhairn. The Falkirk Local History Society states that James Shaw and his wife, Agnes Fleming, were granted a charter from Alexander, Earl of Linlithgow, in 1613 which contained the privilege of "constructing a mill in that part of Dalquhairne." The family supported the Jacobites in the 1715 uprising and as a punishment, most of their estate apart from thirty acres surrounding Dalquairn was forfeited by the Government. In the twentieth century, the house stood derelict for many years after the last of the Shaw family died out. By 1972, it was so dangerous the walls were demolished.

No doubt William had dealings with Charles Shaw during the construction or maybe he lodged with them as Avonbridge is very near Causewayend. Shaw must have thought William a presentable young man who was starting to take an interest in one of his daughters, Janet. On 3rd August 1839 William and Janet were married in Slamannan church. At this time in the nineteenth century, there was a surplus of women. Often they were condemned to being spinsters, "left on the shelf." The word Slamannan may come from the Gaelic meaning "the back of the world." It is still a bit like this even today because the railway closed in 1930. The influx of men during the construction would have been a godsend to the women of the area longing for the love of a man. Charles Shaw had one daughter off his hands and a new life was opening up for both.

The Slammanan Railway opened a year later in August 1840.

Janet Shaw, William Paterson's wife, in later life.
(Anne-Mary Paterson collection)

BACK IN THE HIGHLANDS

In 1839, married and starting a career as a civil engineer, William returned to Inverness as Joseph Mitchell's assistant. Was this what was always planned? We do not know. Murdoch, the youngest in the family, was just thirteen and at school at Inverness Academy. Their father, Donald, was still farming at Dell of Inshes.

The Highland road system was gradually improving under the direction of Joseph Mitchell for the Commission for Highland Roads and Bridges. Telford died in 1834 but Joseph was dreaming of better communications for Inverness with the outside world. Telford was a canal man. When he was offered the job of engineer on the Liverpool & Manchester Railway, he felt he could not betray his canal clients and continued his work on canals and roads. He would have realised the potential of railways and that they would outstrip canals but, nearing the end of his career and in his seventies, he decided to leave railway matters to younger men.

In 1837 and 1838, Joseph was involved in one of the proposed plans for a railway line from Glasgow to Edinburgh. It was to pass close to the Earl of Hopetoun's property so was not to his lordship's liking. His agent, James Hope, employed Joseph to carry out a survey to find a less obtrusive route. Joseph produced another route but nothing came of it. The Edinburgh & Glasgow promoters decided on a more level route via Falkirk which was opened in 1842 and put paid to any of the grand plans to include the Slamannan Railway on a route between the two cities.

Joseph heard that the government had instructed John Macneill to carry out a survey in Ireland to identify possible railways so he suggested to Provost Nicol of Inverness a similar survey for the Highlands. Joseph considered that the persons most familiar with the terrain of the North of Scotland were the employees of the Commissioners for Highland Roads and Bridges, Joseph being the chief surveyor. Sadly, the Treasury in London did not see this as a necessity and the idea came to nothing.

Joseph Mitchell had experience of surveying for roads and building bridges but not of building railways so needed someone with that knowledge. Taking on William as a young man with this experience, probably engineered by Joseph himself, would seem a good idea especially as he was a local boy.

William's older brother John had gone off to Canada where he was trying to establish himself as a dry goods merchant so William probably regarded himself as the head of the family and should be in Inverness.

William and Janet settled into a house at 11 Wells Street in Inverness. A terrace house in a street must have been a great contrast for Janet who was used to living in the country. However the census of April 1841 shows that her sister Elizabeth was living with them. As she was unmarried, she was company for Janet as William had a lot of work on the roads and bridges to to take him away from home much of the time. Janet was pregnant at the time and gave birth to another Elizabeth the following June. We do not know how well William was paid but their fairly humble home plus only one fifteen year old servant would suggest not very great wealth. Janet gave birth to another daughter, Margaret, in April 1843.

Joseph was still dreaming of his railways in the Highlands. In 1842, a solicitor who acted for some of the landowners at meetings of the Commissioners for Highland Roads and Bridges complained about the cost of the road maintenance and their administration. Joseph Mitchell, no doubt affronted at the attack on his integrity and professional skills, suggested that the Commissioners set up an investigation; that started in February 1842. The committee took ten months over their deliberations, which involved producing many documents about expenditure and there were inspections causing a lot of extra work for both William and Joseph. In October, the committee reported that the roads were in a good state and that repairs cost less than for similar roads elsewhere.

Murdoch left Inverness Academy in 1844 with some distinction, winning prizes in Arithmetic, Greek and Geography which also included the Use of Globes. He then took a post in the Inverness branch of Bell Rannie & Co, Edinburgh wine merchants, presumably as some sort of clerk. This work gave him a grounding in business that was to prove useful to him in his future career but it was not really to his taste. In 1846, he decided on a change when William suggested to him that civil engineering might be a more suitable calling and he became apprenticed to Joseph Mitchell.

In March 1845 Janet gave birth to another daughter, also called Janet. Railway mania was at its height. Lines were being proposed all over the country. Some were very impractical, just figments of speculators' imaginations but others were more realistic. Joseph's dream was to build a railway from Perth over the Pass of Druimuachdar, which was nearly fifteen hundred feet high, then north to Nairn and along the coast to Inverness. He desperately wanted the line to be the one he designed, but as was commonplace, there were competitors. The railway north to Aberdeen was authorised in 1845 so the Great North of Scotland Railway planned to build a line from Aberdeen to Inverness that would provide access for Inverness passengers and freight to the south by a longer but less hilly route. Another company, the Direct Northern Railway, put forward a line from Perth to west of Elgin via Braemar and Tomintoul. Joseph must have felt he had an edge over everyone else. He knew his route very well because of his work on the road from Perth to Inverness. His railway roughly followed this route.

There were of course problems with the proprietors of estates that the line was planned to pass through. The Duke of Atholl's agent objected and so did the Earl of Seafield as the railway passed

The railway near Dalwhinnie photographed in 1960 looking north but demonstrating the wild and lofty scenery through which the railway passes. The old A9 is on the right.   *(H C Casserley)*

through his estates near Grantown–on-Spey; Joseph describes in his *Reminiscences* a visit to the Earl at Cullen House, on one of his other estates, to placate the situation. He employed between seventeen and twenty surveyors on the job. The minimum pay was two guineas a day but there was such a shortage that it was sometimes necessary to pay as much as five guineas.

Bills for new railways, including detailed plans, had to be deposited in Parliament by midnight on 30th November for consideration during the ensuing session. As the deadline approached things would have got more hectic. Surveys needed checking and every minute detail that would help the cause had to be included.

So on 1st February 1846, Joseph, his wife and William set off to London to present their case to Parliament. On another of Joseph's visits to London in connection with Inverness Harbour, he tells us that the journey took fourteen days. This presumably was by land. A steamer, the North Star, did the journey by sea in just under a week but only ran from March to October. This was probably not to everyone's taste whatever the time of year. The Royal Mail Coach was the only one that ran throughout the year to Perth. It left at one forty-five a.m. and arrived in Perth at twelve thirty a.m. next day. The fare inside was two pounds five shillings.

After over two months in London, Joseph and William appeared before the parliamentary committee dealing with their application on April 29th. The members threw out the Bill because they considered the gradients too steep for the locomotives at that time. The ascent to Druimuachdar at one thousand four hundred and eighty-four feet was unprecedented.

Joseph said in his *Reminiscences*, "As may be supposed, I was much down cast and disheartened at such a termination to all our labours. I took my faithful assistant Paterson (who had worked night and day on our plans) and my wife to Oxford and Gloucester, and so home."

A rare insight into William's life survives in a letter dated 13th October 1847 to his brother John in Canada. John had displeased his family back home by marrying a Roman Catholic woman and consequently he probably did not write to the family as often as he should, especially his parents. William says, "In 1845 & 6 we were very busy with the Perth & Inverness Railway & Inverness & Elgin Railway surveys which kept us wonderfully busy for many a month. I had not above 4½ hours sleep nightly. I was in London for some 14 weeks in spring and summer of last year but was very busy there – However I saw a great many sights notwithstanding."

In an earlier part of the letter he says, "Your father has been very deaf, & rather dull in consequence about a month or two ago, but he has wonderfully recovered his hearing – although he had to use a trumpet for a short time. Your mother is very poorly with a stomach complaint and a degree of pain in taking food of which she can take but a small quantity – she is rather better and was very poorly for some time. Your father is really vexed at your not writing him at all. It grieves him very much, and he hopes and trusts that you will write him as soon as you possibly can. Nothing I am sure would give him greater satisfaction than to hear from you as he is quite dull about your silence." The original with a postmark was in William's papers. As the family had not heard from John for a while, he may have moved and the letter had been returned. Their mother Elizabeth died not long after this letter, on 28th November 1847 aged fifty-eight, presumably from the stomach problem.

William also sympathises with John and his wife at the loss of their first child and says of his own family, "Mrs Paterson, Lizzy and the little ones are all quite well except Donald, my youngest, now about 6 months old & he is very ill indeed having lost all the skin on his body & is sore all over. Poor fellow he has suffered a great deal and his mother constantly nurses him so that her labour with him is far from being light. I hope however he is getting the turn for the better." William and Janet lost three children in infancy including Donald.

He says that Alexander, their brother, referred to as Sandy, was well and spent a month with them in the autumn and that Murdoch was training with Joseph Mitchell and working hard. He also

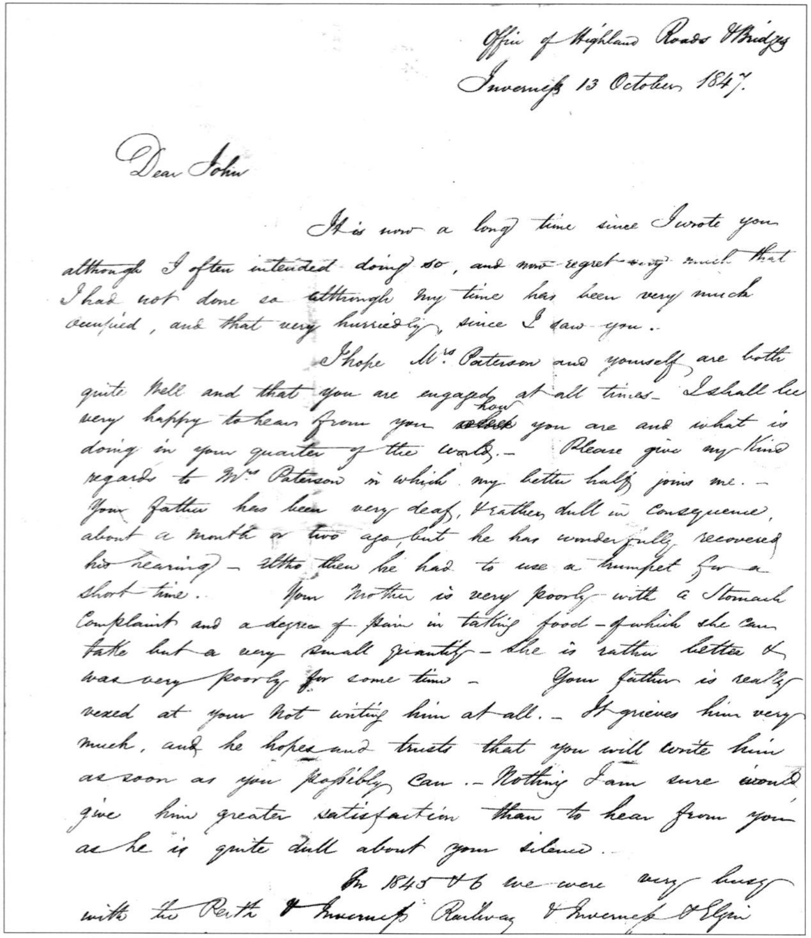

Office of Highland Roads & Bridges
Inverness 13 October 1847.

Dear John

It is now a long time since I wrote you although I often intended doing so, and now regret very much that I had not done so although my time has been very much occupied, and that very hurriedly, since I saw you.–

I hope Mrs Paterson and yourself are both quite well and that you are engaged at all times – I shall be very happy to hear from you how you are and what is doing in your quarter of the world.– Please give my kind regards to Mrs Paterson in which my better half joins me.– Your father has been very deaf, & rather dull in consequence, about a month or two ago, but he has wonderfully recovered his hearing – altho then he had to use a trumpet for a short time. Your Mother is very poorly with a Stomach Complaint and a degree of pain in taking food – of which she can take but a very small quantity – She is rather better & was very poorly for some time – Your father is really vexed at your not writing him at all.– It grieves him very much, and he hopes and trusts that you will write him as soon as you possibly can.– Nothing I am sure would give him greater satisfaction than to hear from you as he is quite dull about your silence.–

In 1845 & 6 we were very busy with the Perth & Inverness Railway & Inverness & Elgin

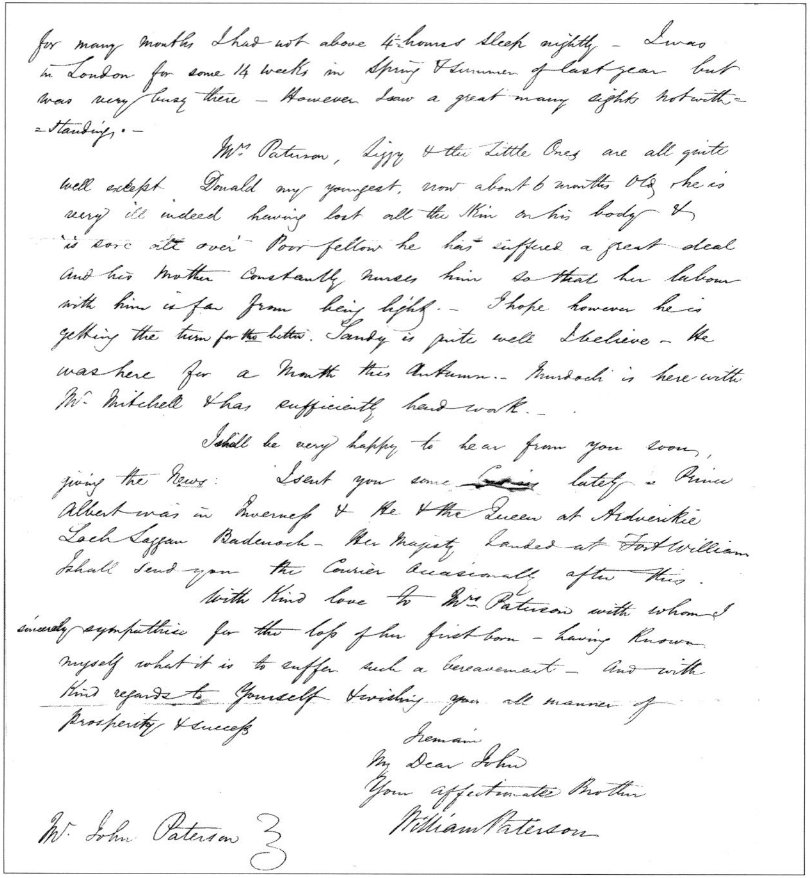

for many months I had not above 4 hours sleep nightly – I was in London for some 14 weeks in Spring & Summer of last year but was very busy there – However saw a great many sights notwithstanding.–

Mrs Paterson, Lizzy & the Little Ones are all quite well except Donald my youngest, now about 6 months old – he is very ill indeed having lost all the skin on his body & is sore all over – Poor fellow he has suffered a great deal and his Mother constantly nurses him so that her labour with him is far from being light.– I hope however he is getting the turn for the better. Sandy is quite well I believe – He was here for a Month this Autumn.– Murdoch is here with Mr Mitchell & has sufficiently hard work.–

I shall be very happy to hear from you soon, giving the News: I sent you some ~~Couriers~~ lately – Prince Albert was in Inverness & He & the Queen at Ardverikie Loch Laggan Badenoch – Her Majesty landed at Fort William I shall send you the Courier occasionally after this.

With kind love to Mrs Paterson with whom I sincerely sympathise for the loss of her first born – having known myself what it is to suffer such a bereavement – And with kind regards to Yourself & wishing you all manner of prosperity & success

I remain
My Dear John
Your affectionate Brother
William Paterson

Mr John Paterson

Letter from William Paterson to his brother in Canada.

mentioned that Prince Albert had been in Inverness and that Queen Victoria had visited Ardverikie on Loch Laggan. This was a property she and Albert considered buying before purchasing Balmoral. They ruled it out because of the rain and the midges. It is now more famous as "Glenbogle" in the television series "Monarch of the Glen."

Joseph and William were obviously disappointed at the failure of their project, so much so that Joseph published a statement about the engineering and the estimated traffic. It was widely circulated and he says, "It germinated in the minds of the public, and greatly assisted in showing the accuracy of my calculations, and the importance to the northern counties of a railway through the central Highlands."

Railway mania abruptly ended in 1846 as banks became worried about their loans and many approved schemes were abandoned for lack of capital. Joseph and William returned to their work on roads, bridges and harbours. This included planning improvements to Inverness Harbour that involved another trip to London for Joseph, but not accompanied by William this time.

In his *Reminiscences of Inverness*, John Fraser tells us that the winter of 1848 and 1849 was very stormy with rain and snow. Joseph says that prior to 25th January 1849, it rained for three whole days, and the river Ness rose alarmingly to heights never witnessed before. The river overflowed its banks and houses on the west side were flooded to two to three feet. Joseph went to Loch Ness to examine the entrance to the Caledonian Canal at Dochgarroch. The lock there regulates the level of water entering the canal from Loch Dochfour on its last stretch before reaching the sea at Clachnaharry. Joseph found a breach of one hundred and fifty feet in the canal bank. The canal engineer was trying to stem the floodwater with trees, brushwood and gravel. Water was discharging from the canal into the river causing even more flooding in the river. The level continued to rise alarmingly until the high tide due one hour after midnight. As the tide started to go out the floodwaters still kept on rising and houses in Inverness on both banks of the river Ness were flooded.

Everyone was watching the old stone bridge of seven arches beneath the castle which was built in 1684 and painted by J M W Turner in about 1833 on his tour of Scotland. The principal river crossing, it shook and trembled as the waters rose. Just after six, the flood reached the keystone of the central arch. The arch on the town side collapsed, followed almost immediately by the other arches. A drunken sailor staggering home quite oblivious of the excitement and the danger, was the last person to cross it. Further downstream was a wooden bridge called the Black Bridge on the site of the present Waterloo Bridge. So for the town's inhabitants this was the only way left to cross the river other than by boat. Joseph Mitchell, William and Murdoch must have had a very busy night.

The town council blamed the alterations made to the entrance to the canal at Dochgarroch for their vicissitudes and requested Joseph to look into the matter. They instructed Joseph to employ another engineer to help him. Joseph selected a Mr Leslie from Edinburgh. They duly decided that the canal entrance from Loch Ness was the problem and that modifications were required. In the meantime, Joseph and William designed a temporary timber footbridge to replace the old stone bridge. The provost, the town clerk and Joseph had to go to London to get a new bridge sanctioned. They appeared before the Chancellor of the Exchequer who ordered that a Mr Rendall should look into the replacement. It ended up that Mr Rendall, not Joseph, got the job of designing a new bridge, a suspension bridge. It took five years to complete after a lot of extra expenditure on the foundations.

Joseph in a footnote in his *Reminiscences* says,

"Being a local or country engineer, in some of the important works which I had to do, it was desirable to have my plans and recommendations confirmed by men of acknowledged experience and name. I am sorry to say, in almost every case, those consulted attempted to usurp the employment.

"During all my professional life, it required no small tact to stave off such usurpations; and I was pretty successful in keeping in hand my own professional preserves in the northern counties of Scotland."

He was obviously bitter about this matter, especially as Mr Rendall had first recommended a box girder and then a suspension bridge so that the new bridge would not have piers in the river. Joseph pointed out in his memoirs written later that he built a stone bridge of five arches for the Inverness to Dingwall Railway which was opened in 1862. Maybe Mr Rendall does have the last laugh as the floods on the Ness in February 1989 swept away Joseph's bridge. Fortunately, no train was on the bridge at the time. Still it was possibly due for replacement after one hundred and sixty seven years.

In early 1851 Murdoch, his apprenticeship with Joseph Mitchell finished, began work with Proudfoot & Croall of Broughty Ferry, the company selected by Joseph Mitchell to carry out the improvements at Inverness Harbour for the sum of £6,469 9s. 8d. The work was desperately needed. A little book dated 1847 entitled *A History and Description of Inverness* tells us that although an Act of Parliament for improvements had been passed in 1808, nothing had happened and "that the accommodation the harbour affords gives very great dissatisfaction; and that the grossly negligent manner in which it has been managed, has materially affected its revenue." The average revenue for the previous ten years was £880 5s and the average expenditure £211 8s 8d except the year when the steamboat quay was extended when it was £846.

Murdoch was still living at home. Early in 1851 Donald, his father, died aged 73. His older brother James carried on farming Dell of Inshes. This was to be a sad year because on 5th June, James' wife, Jane died aged 21 following the birth of their son, also called Donald. James' second marriage to Mary Munro was at the end of 1852 but there were no more children.

Murdoch, now established in a job and able to support a wife, married Jane MacCallum in January 1852 in Aberdeen. Jane's father was a tax inspector and so was Murdoch's brother, Alexander or Sandy as he was known. One assumes that this is how they met. Jane's mother was a Stewart from Glen Muick on Deeside, a family with a long association with the glen. Sandy married Catherine Dewar in 1850 while working in Perth. He later moved to Edinburgh. He and Catherine had three children, two daughters and a son, while living in Perth.

By 1851 William and Janet had moved to Hawthorn Cottage, Gordon Terrace, but tragedy was to strike again with their children when Elizabeth, their eldest daughter died, aged ten years. The other Elizabeth, Janet's sister, was still living with them.

Donald, another brother of William and Murdoch and my great grandfather, was married to Margaret Mackenzie. By 1851, he was farming on his own account at Balrobert, outside Inverness. By this time, they had three children, a son and two daughters; the youngest, Barbara, was born in February of that year. When grown up Barbara married James Maclean, a brother of my maternal great grandmother. In later years James became stationmaster at Aviemore. Donald and Margaret were to end up with nine surviving children.

Things were not going to plan at the harbour. Proudfoot & Croall were declared insolvent early in 1852. Joseph Mitchell and the Harbour Trustees were so pleased with Murdoch's work that they appointed him to complete the job, which he did to the full satisfaction of everyone. One improvement was to build a bar out into the Beauly Firth, presumably to provide better protection for vessels entering the river in a west wind. The bar is still there, having stood up to gales for many years.

The harbour finished, Joseph was not going to lose such a promising engineer so he asked Murdoch to return to work for him. This was to be the beginning of a career for both brothers in railway building.

The end of 1853 was a time of celebration for Murdoch and Jane when Elizabeth, their first child, came into the world on 23rd December.

BIRTH OF A HIGHLAND RAILWAY

The Great North of Scotland Railway intimated in 1851 that due to shortage of funds they would not be building their line all the way to Inverness, only as far as Huntly. So there did not seem any prospect of Inverness having rail communication with Aberdeen or further south unless someone else did something about it. During 1851 and 1852, a committee formed by Joseph Mitchell looked into the matter. Joseph, Peter Anderson, an Inverness solicitor, and Eneas Mackintosh of Raigmore, a local landowner, went to London to see if any railway company in England was interested in building railways in the north of Scotland. They spoke to the directors of the company who at that time were constructing the railway from Lancaster to Carlisle, now part of the West Coast main line. No one had sufficient funds to help so they realised they would have to raise the money locally.

The committee decided that as the first stage of a line to the south, they would build a railway from Inverness to Nairn. Plans already existed as Nairn was on the route to the south that had been thrown out in 1846. There were no great engineering difficulties as the route passed through fairly flat agricultural land. There were difficulties with one person, a Mr Welsh who lived in Millburn House just on the outskirts of Inverness. He complained that the railway would damage his property. His objections were overruled as nearly every one else welcomed this new mode of transport. Joseph and William were determined to build a railway suited to local requirements and traffic. Lines in the south were costing up to thirty-five thousand pounds per mile; Joseph's target was eight thousand eight hundred and fifty pounds including the purchase of land.

William now had a fifteen and a half mile railway to build and could put his experience in Ireland and Central Scotland to good use. Joseph and he were both so pleased with Murdoch's progress that they appointed him as resident engineer. On 21st September 1854, amid great rejoicing and huge crowds, the Countess of Seafield, wife of the seventh Earl, cut the first turf with an ornamental spade

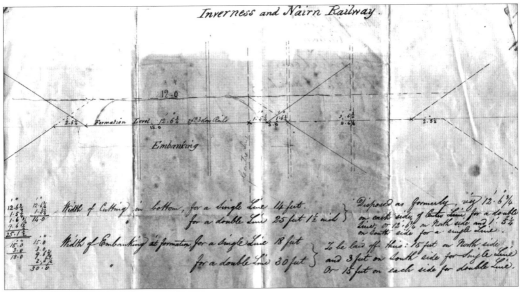

Cross-sections of Cuttings and Embanking, Inverness & Nairn Railway. (*William Paterson's Papers*)

just east of Millburn House. The chairman of the railway was Cluny MacPherson, chief of the Clan MacPherson. Several other local landowners and members of the public subscribed to the funds.

Building a railway detached from other railways was a problem, as all the materials had to come by sea. If a delivery was incorrect, getting the goods exchanged or modified was slow and difficult. While Murdoch was busy sorting this out, Jane was pregnant again. Their son Donald was born on 17th October 1855.

The opening date for the railway was supposed to be 1st August 1855 but there were difficulties in getting the turntables and signalling equipment delivered and when they arrived the order was incomplete. Eventually everything was ready.

On the day of the opening, 5th November 1855, a train of about 30 varied vehicles, some open trucks fitted with seats, set off at noon from the sixty-yard long platform at Inverness Station. The locomotive, designed by Alexander Allan, was called *Raigmore*, after one of the directors, Mackintosh of Raigmore. The train went very slowly at first so that the crowds gathered by the line could see this new spectacle. As it reached out into the country, it gathered speed up to thirty miles per hour. Some passengers got quite nervous, never having travelled at this speed before. It must also have been a bit cold due to the time of year. The return journey from Nairn was at three in the afternoon, and took just one hour. By this time, the passengers were in a very cheerful mood and some sang songs.

The line was single track with no passing loops but the railway company purchased enough land to double the line if required with the bridges built to accommodate this. The sleepers were wooden, laid at right angles to the iron rails. The ballast was gravel or ash. The Highland Railway used this type of ballast until after it was amalgamated into the London Midland & Scottish Railway in 1923. There were four stations, now closed, including Fort George (later Gollanfield) to serve the army barracks built by the Duke of Cumberland after the Battle of Culloden. If passengers wished to continue to Aberdeen from Nairn there was a horse drawn coach connection to Huntly where it connected with the Great North of Scotland Railway.

The viaduct over the river at Nairn on the line eastward to Forres consisted of four arches of 55ft span.
(Whyte, Inverness)

An early photograph of the viaduct over the Findhorn west of Forres. This view is difficult to appreciate today as it is obscured by trees. *(Highland Railway Society/Roberts colln)*

Fired up by their success Joseph decided to carry on to Elgin. This was not without problems. There was still no railway between Elgin and Huntly to provide a through service to Aberdeen. The Great North of Scotland Railway, having previously said that they could not afford a line beyond Huntly, decided to continue on to Keith. This extension opened on 10th October 1856. The two railway companies finally came to an agreement that the Great North of Scotland would pay £40,000 towards the cost of the line from Nairn to Keith. The new company, called the Inverness & Aberdeen Junction Railway, was authorised on 21st July 1856.

William had much to do with the design of this line in collaboration with Joseph. There were three major rivers to cross, two being the Nairn at the town of Nairn and the Findhorn near Forres. Beyond Elgin the line takes a big sweep inland to reach Keith by crossing the third, the Spey at Orton. Murdoch was again appointed resident engineer during the construction. As this work was much further away than Nairn, Jane and Janet would have had to get used to their husbands being away from home.

The Nairn viaduct is of stone with four arches. According to Joseph it was "heavy and formidable" as it was difficult to find rock for the foundations. In some places, they had to excavate between six and ten feet to find a solid foundation.

The viaduct over the river Findhorn, west of Forres, has three one hundred and fifty foot spans that are early examples of an open-top box girder constructed of butt jointed wrought-iron plates. The piers are forty-six and a half feet above the bed of the river and it was necessary to excavate eighteen feet to find rock for the foundations. Because of its good workmanship, it is still in use after a century and a half. Until the viaduct was completed, a temporary station called Dalvey was opened on the west side of the river Findhorn on 22nd December 1857 so that the line from Nairn could earn some revenue. Everything was ready for the opening to Elgin on 25th March 1858.

The extension from Elgin to Keith, however, posed problems at the crossing over the river Spey at Orton. The Spey was the biggest river they had to cross. It is in places one of the fastest flowing rivers in Britain and has a huge catchment area. Telford built his famous suspension bridge further upstream at Craigellachie but by the time it reaches Orton near the sea, the Spey is a much bigger river. The railway viaduct took much longer to complete than the rest of the line and for a time temporary scaffolding carried the rails on the central span which was of wrought iron girder construction, two hundred and thirty feet wide with six side arches on the western side for floodwater.

When the line opened on 18th August 1858 the Board of Trade would not allow trains carrying passengers to cross the viaduct. Fortunately, there was a road bridge close by so passengers detrained, walked over the adjacent bridge and got back into the train which had run empty across the bridge. In the first plan, the viaduct was to be thirty feet higher but Joseph and William, on further examination of the surrounding countryside, found that if they increased the gradient east of the viaduct from one in one hundred to one in sixty, they could lower the bridge height and save fifty thousand pounds. By the turn of the twentieth century, the viaduct was life expired. The replacement was opened in 1906.

While the line to Keith was being completed Joseph was asked to make a preliminary survey for a railway from Inverness north to Dingwall. The moving spirit for this line was Alexander Matheson of Ardross who was already chairman of the Inverness & Aberdeen Junction, but who owned estates north of Dingwall and on the west coast on Loch Carron. Alexander's uncle was one of the founders of Jardine Matheson, a company that operated in China and India. He had accumulated great wealth doing trade between the two. Alexander Matheson was also a director and had made his own money, some of which was to be put to good use in the establishment of railways in the North of Scotland.

In January 1859, Alexander convened a meeting to form a committee to consider this undertaking and it instructed Joseph to carry out a survey for submission to Parliament. The land following the coast round the Beauly and Cromarty Firths is mainly agricultural and relatively flat but the line had to cross the Caledonian Canal and three rivers, the Ness, the Beauly and the Conon. William and Murdoch were heavily involved in the survey. After leaving Inverness, the railway went over an embankment constructed over a small bay in the Beauly Firth. It then crossed a swing bridge over the Caledonian Canal and then squeezed itself between the village of Clachnaharry and the steep hillside to its south.

A wooden bridge spanned the river Beauly. At the Conon, adjacent to what was then a Telford

Beauly Station looking north towards the footbridge and road bridge. The large station building here, erected in 1875, included a private waiting room for Lord Lovat.   *(J L Stevenson)*

road bridge, the stone viaduct has five arches with seventy-three foot spans on a skew of forty-five degrees to the river. The north abutment is three hundred and four feet downstream from the south abutment. A series of right-angled stone ribs spans from pier to pier. Joseph considered this crossing to be a great feat of bridge engineering. Whose idea it was he does not disclose in his *Reminiscences*. Sadly, he is not very good at giving credit to the other people involved and only mentions William and Murdoch a few times.

The line to Dingwall opened in June 1862 and to Invergordon in May 1863. While Murdoch was busy as resident engineer on this line, William was assisting Joseph with the surveys for a line from Forres to Dunkeld in Perthshire. The Perth & Dunkeld Railway opened in April 1856 and was worked by a completely separate company, the Scottish Midland Junction Railway, but it was a step northwards from Perth. There was a lot of dissatisfaction with the arrangements at Aberdeen on the existing route from Inverness as, unlike the present day, there were two stations. Goods and passengers had to be transferred from one to the other; that took a lot of time and sometimes meant an overnight stay in Aberdeen. Joseph and William resurrected the 1846 plans for the Nairn to Perth railway. They proposed that it branched off south from Forres, the next town eastwards from Nairn, because it would pick up extra passengers and freight from Elgin and the populated coastal areas of the Moray Firth.

Some landowners like Mackintosh of Mackintosh and MacPherson of Glentruim in Badenoch were so keen on the railway passing through their estates that they offered land for nothing while others such as the Duke of Atholl were more antagonistic. Joseph in his *Reminiscences* gives an amusing account of his visit to Blair Castle in the summer of 1860. The Duke was rather eccentric and though dinner was supposed to be at eight o'clock, he did not appear until ten o'clock. The following day Joseph took the Duke and the Duchess to show them the line of the railway along which he had arranged white flags. The Duke agreed to the railway, Joseph said, after pressure from his wife. Most of the viaducts in Perthshire have decorations to please the Duke.

Amongst William's papers is a letter written on a Monday, but undated, from Dunkeld Palace, another residence of the Duke. It says, "The Duke and Duchess will leave Dunkeld about four thirty this afternoon & drive up the road towards the Haughs. If Mr Paterson would come down by the Mail till he meet the Carriage he could then return up the Road with the Duke & Duchess & point out the Line of the proposed Railway." This presumably was a similar exercise to Joseph's at Blair Atholl but no mention is made of William staying at Dunkeld Palace or even seeing the inside of it.

Although the line from Perth was called the Perth & Dunkeld the station was and still is at Birnam, a village across the Tay from Dunkeld on the Murthly Estates. A previous Duke commissioned Telford to build a very fine bridge across the Tay from Birnam to Dunkeld. One of the Duke's objections was the loss of tolls if the railway went through Dunkeld itself. The Highland Boundary Fault runs just south of Dunkeld and there is an abrupt change of scenery from mainly pastoral land to the grandeur of the Highlands. It is understandable that the Duke would be worried about the intrusion of trains into this landscape. Just north of Dunkeld the line crosses the river Braan by a bridge which was decorated with turrets above the piers and then enters the short Inver Tunnel, which has a rather more fancy entrance than normal. There is another short tunnel at the Pass of Killiecrankie where in 1689 the Jacobite army defeated the government forces of King William III. Here the river Garry passes through a narrow gorge with little room for a railway so the track is on a viaduct suspended from the hillside before it enters the tunnel.

Further north beyond Blair Atholl at Struan, the Calvine viaduct must be unique in that it spans both a road bridge and the river Garry at the same time. This was also to appease the Duke and not spoil one of his favourite walks. The line then crosses the first summit at Druimuachdar, the highest point on a main line in Britain, and descends into the Spey Valley. It follows this through Kingussie to

Several of the viaducts on the southern section of the Inverness & Perth Junction were given extra decoration to satisfy the Duke of Atholl. The viaduct over the Tilt at Blair Atholl had decorated archways at each end. This drawing shows the original design which differed in detail from the version executed.
(Blair Castle Archives)

Grantown-on-Spey, where it heads north to cross the second summit at Dava before descending once again to Forres. Joseph agreed to build a pretty lodge at an entrance to Castle Grant, near to where the line entered the Earl of Seafield's park at Grantown-on-Spey.

Parliamentary approval of the Inverness & Perth Junction Railway was obtained on 22nd July 1861 and Lady Seafield once again performed the ceremony of cutting the first sod at Forres on 17th October.

The Invergordon line was not completed till March 1863 and the whole route from Forres to Dunkeld was opened in September 1863. Joseph said this was "the busiest part of his life." The Hon T C Bruce, who was chairman of the Inverness & Perth Junction Railway, was always urging Joseph

The Tilt Viaduct at Blair Atholl as seen from the north bank of the river with the decorations added for the benefit of the Duke of Atholl's residence nearby at Blair Castle. The octagonal piers in the sketch have been replaced by square ones and the detail above the arch simplified.   *(Keith Fenwick)*

Calvine Viaduct at Struan, which obliquely crosses the road bridge and the river Garry. A steel girder bridge was built on the other side in 1901 when the line was doubled. (Anne-Mary Paterson)

and William to hurry up and complete the work as it was a drain on the finances. The quicker the work was completed and the line opened the better, so that it could earn money. They wanted to get some of the summer tourist traffic in 1863. Joseph wrote to him begging, "He would not press too much the willing horse." As a result of the strain Joseph suffered a stroke on 4th May 1862 and lost the use of his left side. However, after a month, to the surprise of his doctors, he was able to walk across his room. By July he was well enough to go to London and then to Norwood and Brighton for recuperation. He returned to Inverness in September and was back at work by the end of the year. William and Murdoch were in charge during his absence. Joseph now felt he needed to formalise their

The Tay Viaduct near Dalguise has large turrets above the piers. (Keith Fenwick)

Two plaques on the inside of the parapet of the Divie Viaduct record those involved in the building of the line, including the directors, contractors and engineers. William Paterson's name can just be identified next to that of his boss, Joseph Mitchell.
(Keith Fenwick)

assistance and took both William and Murdoch into partnership, forming Joseph Mitchell & Co.

Building the line from Forres to Perth was a massive undertaking. It climbs long gradients, up to one in seventy, and to a height of nearly fifteen hundred feet at Druimuachdar, unknown for a railway in Scotland, crosses bogs and massive rivers. Work continued in summer and winter, in snow or fine weather. There were seven different contracts with five contractors involved, which meant that construction was going on all the time along the line. In places, particularly in the Pass of Killiecrankie and along the valley of the river Garry, there was so little space for the railway that retaining walls, one as high as fifty-five feet, had to be built to carry the track. Masons and labourers did most of the work by hand, as little machinery was available in those days. In spite of these difficulties, the line was complete two years after letting the contracts. It opened in September 1863. The directors were so anxious for it to start earning money that in spite of objections from Joseph and his partners, it was opened without proper testing and consequently it was not without problems and engine breakdowns.

The 1861 Act included a branch line from Ballinluig to Aberfeldy but work did not start on it until December 1863. It was an expensive line to build, requiring many bridges, including substantial

The Divie Viaduct at Dunphail was the largest on the line from Forres to Grantown-on-Spey. Trains stopped running in 1965 but the viaduct still stands and is used as part of the Dava Way, a footpath from Forres to Grantown-on-Spey.   *(Anne-Mary Paterson)*

The handsome lodge built for the Earl of Seafield at Castle Grant on the road from Grantown-On-Spey to Forres where it is crossed by the railway. A short platform was provided here. (Anne-Mary Paterson)

viaducts over the rivers Tummel and Tay, and some eight hundred thousand cubic yards of cut and fill. The branch opened in July 1865.

The portals of the crossing of the river Tay near Ballinluig appear from a distance to resemble the viaducts on the main line that are castellated to appease the Duke of Atholl. On closer inspection, they are fakes made of metal. Although the line is now closed, the locals still use it as an unadopted crossing of the Tay.

On August 1st 1865, the Highland Railway was formed by the amalgamation of the Inverness & Aberdeen Junction and Inverness & Perth Junction Railways. The Perth & Dunkeld Railway was absorbed. Previously, the Inverness & Aberdeen Junction had taken over the Nairn and Ross-shire Railways.

Not content with their efforts south of Inverness the railway was pressing north from Invergordon.

Logierait Viaduct carried the Aberfeldy branch over the Tay. This line is closed but the bridge is still in use and has been restored for local road use by a private trust. It has fake turrets of iron.

(Anne-Mary Paterson)

Ardgay in 1992. This was originally called Bonar Bridge after the town on the other side of the bridge. Several stations between Dingwall and Bonar Bridge had similar large station buildings which included accommodation for the station master and his family.   *(Keith Fenwick)*

Parliament approved an extension to Bonar Bridge in May 1863. The country through which it passes is fairly flat and did not pose many engineering difficulties. This line opened in October 1864 and again Joseph, William and Murdoch were the engineers.

While all this frenzied activity of railway building was going on Joseph was still General Inspector to the Highland Roads and Bridges Commission. We do not know how Joseph divided the work but it would seem in the light of future events that the principal assistant in this work was William and that Murdoch undertook most of the railway supervision, especially after Joseph's illness. In the June following Joseph's illness he received notice that the grant from Parliament for the roads and bridges would cease. The maintenance was now to fall to each county, which meant that before the handover every road and bridge required inspection, all necessary repairs completed, and maps produced. Joseph was not able to do the physical inspections himself so qualified staff, probably under the supervision of William, had to be employed. The Commission started under Thomas Telford in 1803-4 and this piece of history ended sixty years later in 1863.

There was still no railway to the west coast of the Highlands. James Robert Hope Scott, a parliamentary barrister, who had purchased an estate on Loch Shiel near Fort William, thought a line from Kingussie to Fort William would be a good idea so he asked Thomas Bouch, later designer of the ill-fated Tay Railway Bridge, to do a quick survey. Joseph had always thought that a more sensible terminus would be at Kyleakin Ferry opposite Skye. When a group of landowners, including Alexander Matheson who owned estates near Plockton and who was now chairman of the Highland Railway, formed a committee to promote the Kyleakin idea, nothing more was heard of the Hope Scott idea. At Kyleakin David Hutcheson's (predecessors of David MacBrayne) steamers passed daily on their way to and from Glasgow and the Hebrides. The committee instructed Joseph Mitchell & Co to do a survey for the line. It is widely considered that Murdoch was in charge of the survey due to Joseph's poor health.

Northwards the railway had reached as far as Bonar Bridge. In June 1865, an extension to Brora was proposed as the Sutherland Railway. The chairman was the Duke of Sutherland. The line passed near his castle at Dunrobin, north of Golspie. Joseph Mitchell & Co had surveyed this line, which in practical terms meant that Murdoch carried it out. The Bill for the Sutherland Railway passed through Parliament in July 1865. Due to shortage of money and many arguments, construction did not start until after Joseph's retirement in 1867.

The Duke had a great friend, Kenneth Murray of Geanies who was a local bank agent and a farmer in the Tain area. Murray was one those people who, according to himself, knew about everything including railways. The Duke listened to his opinions rather than to those of the experts. The Duke decided, with Joseph's approval, to consult John Fowler who had recently bought an estate near Ullapool and who some years later was the joint engineer with Benjamin Baker for the Forth Railway Bridge. Unfortunately, through some sort of misunderstanding, the Duke got the impression that John Fowler thought Joseph's work was too extravagant, especially his bridges. Joseph, not unnaturally, took exception to this, as his lines were mostly cheaper per mile than other railways. John Fowler said he would put things right with the Duke but forgot or failed to do so. Things got even worse when the Duke publicly accused Joseph and his partners of extravagance at a meeting of the Highland Railway Board in Inverness. Because of all this, the Duke appointed Murray to oversee the work. The line though approved to Brora stopped short at Golspie due to lack of funds.

In November 1866, Joseph went to Italy on the advice of his doctor. When he returned to Inverness in May 1867, he found that under the supervision of Murdoch the line was nearly complete. Murdoch however had found the work very difficult due to the interference from Mr Murray. This must have been a very worrying time for Murdoch as Jane his wife took ill around April 1867 with what was to prove a terminal illness.

As a result of the interference of Murray, Joseph Mitchell & Co tendered their resignation as engineers and William Baxter took over the work of completing the Sutherland Railway which opened on 13th April 1868. At this point Joseph retired.

On this section there are two stations, Culrain and Invershin, which are only half a mile apart. Between these stations is the Oykell Viaduct which crosses the Kyle of Sutherland. As the nearest road crossing is at Bonar Bridge, involving a detour of around seven miles, this wrought iron lattice girder viaduct also provided a short cut for the local inhabitants. The fare was a halfpenny to travel between the stations. Masonry arches, two on the south and three on the north, flank the two hundred and thirty foot single span. The track deck unusually is on top rather than between the trusses. This has enabled in recent years the installation of a pedestrian walkway under the track.

Edderton was just north of Tain. Balblair Distillery was built adjacent to the line and can be seen in the distance in this photograph taken in 1956.

(J L Stevenson)

Joseph Mitchell's career had extended over forty-five years. There is little doubt that his mentor, Thomas Telford, would have been extremely proud of his work and the vision which brought about incredible improvements in transport in the Scottish Highlands, both by road and rail. Until the A9, the Perth to Inverness road, was rebuilt in the 1970s, the system that Joseph put in place had changed little. The railway transformed the Highlands and brought much needed prosperity from tourism and a rapid expansion of new industries such as whisky distilling and forestry.

After he retired Joseph wrote *Reminiscences of My Life in the Highlands* which was published in two volumes in 1883 and 1884. Although they provide an interesting glimpse into his involvement in the development of railways in the Highlands, he was writing about events that had taken place over twenty years previously. Inevitably with the passage of time memory clouds and he may have become more obsessed with his own importance because some of his accounts do not tally with the railway minutes. Maybe it is for this reason that he hardly mentions William and Murdoch or his other, no doubt hard working, members of staff.

The Sutherland Railway took a long detour inland from Bonar Bridge via Lairg but still required the substantial Oykell Viaduct to cross the Kyle of Sutherland between Culrain and Invershin. This view looks upstream, with Culrain on the left and Invershin on the right. What is now the A836 passes under the right-hand arch.
(Highland Railway Society/Roberts collection)

GOING IT ALONE

Joseph Mitchell & Co was dissolved at Joseph's retirement. There were really two businesses, Highland roads and bridges and the railway. William had already taken over the roads and bridges and Murdoch now continued with the railway work. However, William did not completely abandon the railway and an informal partnership seems to have continued, as we will see later on.

At Murdoch's home at Seaview, Millburn, Jane was still ill, probably from some form of cancer. The illness must have been very distressing and uncomfortable and no doubt painful. She died on 8th April 1868. Elizabeth was fourteen and Donald was twelve. These would be difficult times for a father and for his children, especially as he was away from home a lot. We can only guess how they all felt even though death was just around the corner for everyone in those days when medical science was not as it is today. Teenage years have always been a problem time and the death of a mother catastrophic. In addition, people did not speak about illnesses in those days. It was an entirely private matter only spoken about to intimate friends and relations. Often the patient was unaware how serious the illness was, so must have wondered why recovery was so slow. By all accounts, Murdoch

was a friendly man who got on well with everyone and knew many of the people who worked for him by name, so Jane's illness must have been particularly difficult for him when he had to appear cheerful and his usual self in public.

Construction of the Dingwall & Skye Railway had not started. Because of the difficulties with landowners, a resurvey of the proposed line was required with particular attention to the Strathpeffer section and near the western end around Achnashellach. In 1867, the Dingwall & Skye appointed Murdoch as engineer at a salary of £500 per year.

At the Strathpeffer end Sir William Mackenzie of Coul's stipulations for the line were far too expensive. The first plan was for a station on the southern

Raven Rock, Strathpeffer. The railway to Strome had to make an expensive diversion because of objections from Sir William Mackenzie. This involved steep gradients and this deep cutting.
(Highland Railway Society/Roberts Collection)

The Dingwall & Skye Railway terminated at Strome Ferry, where the original overall roof of the station was extant when this photograph was taken in the early 20th century. The extension to Kyle of Lochalsh can be seen disappearing under the road bridge in the distance, while the pier on the right served steamers to Skye and the Outer Isles when Strome Ferry was the terminus. (J L Stevenson collection)

side of Strathpeffer. The line would then travel west and northwest passing within about a quarter of a mile of Coul House. So that his view would not be spoilt, Sir William said he would only agree to the railway going through his estate if it were put in a five hundred and ten yard long landscaped tunnel. Because of the substantial extra cost of this proposal, it became necessary to find another route that would provide some sort of service to Strathpeffer.

This little village was important as a spa. Since the latter part of the 18th Century, its waters were well known. The Royal Society mentioned it in 1770. The sulphurous drinks, along with the thermal baths, were popular with sufferers of rheumatism and other complaints as they found them beneficial. Many of its visitors were local. However, with the increasing popularity of the Highlands and of spas it was seeking visitors from further afield.

The only possible line to appease Sir William was to have a station up on the hillside to the north of the valley. It is over a mile from Strathpeffer up a steep hill. The railway then continues to the summit at Raven Rock at a height of four hundred and fifty eight feet with gradients in places up to one in fifty. Sir William had placed a heavy burden on the railway. The steam trains of those days often needed a banking engine at the back because of the gradient. Passengers for Strathpeffer had to complete their journey to the spa by horse transport. The irony of this saga is that Sir William died shortly before the completion of the line so he would never have seen a train passing by. When the branch to Strathpeffer was later opened, this station was renamed Achterneed.

Achnashellach was the other problem. The local landowner, Captain Tennant, desired that the line should go to the back of his shooting lodge so that his view would not be spoilt. The original plan was to have a steady drop down to Strathcarron. The resulting deviation meant a short climb before dropping down more steeply.

The line was to end at Attadale on Loch Carron. Although the intended terminus was originally to be at what is now Kyle of Lochalsh, it was soon realised that the cost of the engineering work for

The Engineer's Report was always appended to that of the Directors for each half year, but usually just certified that everything was in order. Murdoch Paterson's first report after the opening of the Skye line was much more detailed.

Engineer's Chambers, Inverness, 15th October, 1870

To the Directors of the Dingwall and Skye Railway

Gentlemen – The line from Dingwall to Strome Ferry, 53 miles 7 chains in length, was, as you are aware, opened on 19th August last. The permanent way and works have to be maintained up to 19th February next by the contractors, and I am glad to say that this duty is being well attended to by them, and the line is in good running order. The drains and watercourses are being secured against the winter floods, and the most exposed portions of the sea slopes on Lochcarron shore are being strengthened. The station works, with the exception of two goods sheds, are nearly completed. Cattle pens were erected at the proper time for the loading of sheep and cattle at the various stations. The strengthening of the pier at Strome Ferry is nearly completed. The embanking of the interior, which caused the bulging out and breaking of some of the piles, has been removed, and new piles driven instead. Additional horizontal and diagonal bracings have also been added, and the roadway floored with timber in lieu of the embankment removed. Four new piles have also been driven at the angles of the outer head, to resist blows from steamers, and two gangways have been fitted up for the landing of passengers, sheep and cattle, at low water and half tide. The supplies of water for the engines at Achnasheen and Strome are very satisfactory; but at Garve the water has to be pumped into the tank, as no regular supply can be had by gravitation. I have also a tank and pump in course of erection at Strathcarron Station, to meet the demand should any mishap arise to the supply at Strome – I have the honour to be, gentlemen, your most obedient servant.

MURDOCH PATERSON

the last section was prohibitive because of the large number of deep cuttings required. The rock in that area is very hard. The new Bill for the deviations and providing for a hotel and pier at Attadale was approved in May 1868. This probably meant that Murdoch had to go to London. In the 1861 census, the family had a housekeeper, cook and another servant so they or their successors as well as Murdoch's brothers and sister living in the Inverness area would care for the children.

The first sod was cut at Dingwall at the end in September 1868 and at the western end in October 1868. There were supply problems with the western contract due to stormy weather, as all the materials had to come by sea. The contractors were only able to make a proper start in February 1869. Winter was difficult but so was summer with the proverbial midges.

John Fowler, later co-designer of the Forth Railway Bridge with Benjamin Baker, became a director of the Dingwall & Skye Railway in August 1868. He regarded himself as a kind of honorary consulting engineer who could thwart the best-laid plans. People said that he was a difficult man. He bought the Braemore estate in the Loch Broom area on the Ullapool road.

Fowler was strongly opposed to the railway ending at Attadale and said it should go further down Loch Carron to Strome Ferry. One of the reasons was that the water was much deeper at Strome so larger ships to serve to Skye and the Outer Hebrides could berth there. The rest of the board were opposed to this, as it would be an extra four and a half miles of construction, adding to the cost of a railway that they already had extreme difficulty financing. Nevertheless, on his return from wintering in the Mediterranean in 1869 Fowler won the day at a meeting of the directors on 23rd March in London. Prior to this Murdoch had carried out a survey of the extra mileage.

He had to make considerable savings to stay within the budget before contracting for the extra mileage on the western section. The hotel at Strome was scrapped and it was decided to have only a short unpaved station platform and a wooden pier there. Steel rails were only used at points and crossings, iron elsewhere and the signalling and interlocking was very simple.

Work continued satisfactorily during the summer of 1869 including the construction of the pier at Strome Ferry. The weather broke in October but the contractors still managed to continue. During the next few months, there was progress and, by the spring of 1870, the section along the shore of Loch Carron was completed. The hillside above is unstable. The boulders needed clearing away to the best of the contractor's abilities and the shore stabilised. Murdoch was very pleased with the work. Little did he know that the area would present problems of landslides to this day. The directors had hoped that the line would be ready for its Board of Trade inspection on 15th July. After a meeting of the directors in London on 12th May a letter was sent to Murdoch requesting him to remind the contractors of the powers of the contract and to employ the necessary men to complete it on time.

By June the eastern contract from Dingwall was complete but the contractors on the section between Glen Carron Lodge and Achanalt had not ballasted the rails and some of the sleepers were not secured.

By Thursday 28th July, the line was ready for inspection but the troubles were not over. Murdoch accompanied the inspector, Captain Tyler, and two directors when they started at Dingwall on the Friday. They reached Achanalt that evening. They continued on the Monday, reported by the *Invergordon Times* to be a day of thunder, lightning and rain, and completed the job by the Tuesday evening.

A grand banquet at Strome Ferry was arranged for the opening on August 10th but on the 9th Captain Tyler failed the line for passenger traffic on account of the fencing being incomplete, particularly on the western contract. Those invited to the banquet had a free ride to Strome. On 17th

Strathcarron was one of the original crossing places on the Skye line and was provided with a large station building which included accommodation for the station master and his family. Gifford in 'The Buildings of Scotland' credits Murdoch with responsibility for the design. The platforms were further apart than normal, it is said to accommodate the transport of boats on the line. Since this photograph was taken in 1969, the platforms have been raised.   *(Keith Fenwick)*

August, Murdoch telegraphed the Board of Trade to say that the fencing was complete and the line was opened on the 19th. The grand banquet was rearranged for Wednesday 7th September and held in the wooden engine shed there.

The speeches at the banquet praised Murdoch for "never missing an opportunity of saving expense, when such was possible, consistent with efficiency." The line linked Inverness with the west coast and the islands, and gave new opportunities for the fishing communities to export their produce, not to mention how attractive it was to the Victorian tourist. It was said to be the cheapest in Britain at a cost of £4,500 per mile. For Murdoch it was the first project completely on his own and he had every reason to be proud of it.

During the construction Murdoch's personal life took a turn for the better when he married Frances Mary Wiles in Kensington, London, on 18th January 1870. How he met this good lady is a mystery still to be solved. The 1871 census describes Frances' brother William as an architect and surveyor, so maybe Murdoch met him at Joseph Mitchell's house in London or perhaps he was doing work for the railway in London. Frances' family came from St Neots but moved to London. On the marriage certificate, her father is described as a gentleman and in the 1871 census he is a retired brewer. Murdoch, a widower with a young family, was definitely in need of female assistance and Frances' appearance must have been very welcome. In Victorian times, marriages were not always for love but for convenience. No doubt Murdoch also wanted more children.

In the 1871 census Murdoch and Frances, along with Elizabeth, now eighteen and Donald, fifteen, were living in Inverness at the Citadel somewhere near the harbour. Inverness must have been quite a change for Frances from the far more sophisticated London.

Meanwhile how was William getting on? By this time, he and his family had moved to a commodious house called Larkfield on Southside Road, an upmarket district of town. Inverness started to grow once the railway arrived and the middle classes built villas in an expanding area that became known as "The Hill." Just about this time his daughter Margaret married John Arres-Mather, a farmer whose family came from the Scottish Borders though, for some unknown reason, he was born in Dingwall, Ross-shire. The newly weds went to live on a farm at Hobkirk, Roxburghshire. John also had contacts in Ireland and by the time he died in 1916, he owned estates in the Galway area.

A journal kept by William from July 1869 to June 1870 is amongst the family papers. The first part deals with a spring water supply to the Inverness District Asylum at Craig Dunain, built between 1860 and 1864. There are calculations about the size of tank which take into account evaporation and the dimensions of the lead pipe required; not quite the sort of pipe that would be used today, especially for a mental institution!

There were contracts with various people for the repair of roads. James Mann got a contract for three years for repairing the Culloden road at £102 per annum. Alexander Reid had a contract for the road to Dores on Loch Ness for £79 per annum. William was also busy with the new Dingwall Harbour on the Dingwall Canal. The canal, constructed between 1816 and 1817, was a canalised part of the river Peffery. It had many problems over its life because of silt brought down by the river and changing mud banks in the Cromarty Firth. After the approval of the railway from Dingwall to Invergordon, the town council agreed to a fixed bridge over the canal rather than a swing bridge. The original harbour was upstream from the railway bridge so was no longer accessible for shipping. In 1862, the town council obtained powers from the Board of Trade to abandon the upper part of the canal and, downstream of the railway bridge, to widen and deepen it for the construction of a new harbour.

William's work on the harbour may have had to do with a scheme that the Dingwall & Skye Railway had for transporting fishing boats by rail between Dingwall and Strome Ferry. The plan was

A Victorian view of Dunrobin Burn and Bridge. The construction of this nice solid single arch bridge over the Duke of Sutherland's burn delayed the opening of the portion between Golspie and Dunrobin.
(Highland Railway Society/Roberts collection)

for boats to be taken out of the water on the Dingwall Canal, put on to special wagons and transported to the west to be put back into the water and vice versa. This would have saved fishermen a ten-day journey round the north of Scotland through the stormy and dangerous Pentland Firth or the cost and extra time going by the Caledonian Canal. Because of the financial pressures on the company, purchase of the necessary cranes was put off in 1870 and then the proposal was abandoned.

William seems to have usually worked a six-day week from Monday to Saturday. He was an elder of the Old High Church in Inverness so Sunday was a day of rest. He probably attended church services in the morning and evening. There is no mention of summer holidays!

For some reason he seemed to like to know the altitude of various places and would use an aneroid barometer for the job starting at his home. He says, "Larkfield is supposed to be 90 feet above high water mark." He calculated that the summit of Culloden Moor on the Nairnside Road was 459 + 90 therefore 549 feet, and so on as he went to other places in the area.

On Thursday August 12th, he was at a meeting at the Town Hall to divide Inverness into wards in favour of the new Reform Act. While still busy with the asylum water supply and Dingwall Harbour, he had to start thinking about a special pipe for a sluice entering the Caledonian Canal at Dochgarroch where there had been problems in the 1849 floods. Just at the start of this section of canal, there is a regulating lock that controls the water levels on that section.

After the year had passed William was still calling at the asylum, Dingwall Harbour and Dochgarroch, not to mention the other odd jobs on roads and bridges.

Meanwhile the 3rd Duke of Sutherland was proposing to finance an extension to the railway from

Golspie to Helmsdale so life was also busy for Murdoch. No doubt Murdoch used William Baxter's route from Golspie to Brora but, whilst still busy with the Dingwall & Skye, he must have had to organise the survey of the portion from Brora to Helmsdale as the act for the Duke of Suthlerland's Railway was passed in June 1870. He may have felt he had too much to do because in November 1870 he suggested to the Dingwall & Skye that Mr Wilson, who was the Highland Railway engineer at the time, take over responsibility for that line, relieving him to concentrate on the Duke's railway and the far north lines. The Duke was in such a hurry for the railway to reach his castle at Dunrobin that construction started before parliamentary approval. There were engineering problems between Golspie and Dunrobin with a 1 in 60 climb out of the station and then a high one arch bridge over the Golspie Burn being needed. The line from Dunrobin continued to three quarters of a mile from Helmsdale at Gartymore where there was a temporary station. All was completed in record time in the autumn of 1870. Most of the line was close to the sea so ballast was available from the shore for bottoming. This work included a viaduct over the river Brora and a bridge across the Loth Burn.

The opening the whole line was delayed because of the problems north of Golspie so the Duke decided that his locomotive and some rolling stock should be put on to wagons and hauled along the road by a traction engine to Dunrobin where they could be put back on the track. It must have been exciting and quite a sight. On 17th September the section between Dunrobin and the temporary terminus at Gartymore near Helmsdale had a royal inauguration by Princess Christian of Schleswig-Holstein, a daughter of Queen Victoria. After inspection by the Board of Trade, public services started on 1st November 1870.

The 3rd Duke was very keen on railways and had spent some time learning at the London & North Western Railway Works at Wolverton in Buckinghamshire. To those who know about the Highland Clearances the name of the Dukes of Sutherland is synonymous. The person responsible for the evictions was the 1st Duke, George Granville Leveson-Gower, who acquired almost the whole of the county of Sutherland and Dunrobin Castle through his marriage to the Countess of Sutherland. The Leveson-Gowers acquired a vast fortune from coal and wool businesses in England. Known as "The Great Improver" the 1st Duke cleared much of his vast estates of the indigenous people and

Dunrobin Station, the Duke of Sutherland's personal station as it is today. The wooden shed on the right houses the locomotive Brora, one of three 2 foot gauge locos built for Duke of Sutherland for his Trentham Gardens Railway near Stoke by Bagueley in 1935. It has a diesel engine behind the steam outline

(Anne-Mary Paterson)

Probing a peat bog. In the right-hand picture the rod had sunk 15 feet, probably not the full depth of the bog. (Highland Railway Society/Roberts collection)

installed Lowland Scots who grazed sheep on land they leased in emptied glens. It has to be said that the Duke was not the only landlord carrying out this practice, known as "The Clearances," but his evictions were probably the cruellest. True, with government assistance, he had also organised the construction of thirty-four bridges and four hundred and fifty miles of road.

The 3rd Duke's own private station was at Dunrobin where stops were by request. Passengers could only use it with permission from the Duke or his factor. The Highland Railway took over the working of the line when it was completed on 16th May 1871 but the Duke retained rights to run his own engines and stock over the railway and to have his private carriage attached to the London train at Inverness. A later carriage is now in the National Railway Museum at York.

While Murdoch was organising the construction of the line to Helmsdale, George Loch, the Duke of Sutherland's agent, asked him on 26th October 1870 if he would undertake a survey for a line from Helmsdale to Wick. Plans had to be ready by 30th November for consideration in the 1870-1 session of Parliament. Murdoch told Mr Loch he would have to think about it, as there was not much time. In addition, as no proper maps were available for the area, the survey would have to be more extensive. After a few hours, Murdoch told Mr Loch that he thought he would be able to do the work.

Murdoch had two teenagers and a new wife, no doubt with London ideas, to support and with the uncertainty of being self-employed, could not turn down such an offer. However being a conscientious man and careful of his reputation as a civil engineer he would have had to satisfy himself that the job could be done properly in the short time available.

A company called the Caithness Railway had proposed a line from Wick to Thurso which was approved in 1866. Once the construction was completed, it was then their intention to continue south to join the Sutherland Railway, just approved to Brora. However, they were not able to raise enough money even to start the first line so they abandoned the whole scheme.

Wick is only thirty-five miles along the coast from Helmsdale, but anyone who has travelled over the present coast road will realise the terrain is not suitable for a railway because of the high cliffs and long hills over the Ord of Caithness and at Berriedale. The hard rock precluded any tunnels. The

Caithness Railway had proposed an inland route to a point south of Thurso where the line would join that from Wick to Thurso.

Murdoch's work started on 1st November and in a few days he had engaged about sixty-six surveyors and engineers, about one man per mile of track. To complete the plans work went on night and day. Murdoch delivered the plans and sections all completed and lithographed to the parliamentary agents in London on 26th November, one month after Mr Loch had spoken to him.

The route selected by Murdoch takes a long sweep inland from Helmsdale, going up the Strath of Kildonan following the river Helmsdale to Forsinard through country devoid of most human habitation because of the Clearances. The line then climbs at one in sixty to the summit at the county march between Sutherland and Caithness. It then crosses the Flow Country, a windy and desolate area of peat bog. In recent times financial advisors suggested to some of the very wealthy that, as a tax break, they should plant trees there. The station in this area at Altnabreac still has no proper road serving it, only rough tracks. The Sutherland & Caithness Railway was authorised in July 1871.

William Baxter who had been in charge of the railway to Golspie, superintended the building up the valley of the Helmsdale as far as the county boundary of Sutherland. The section beyond in Caithness had engineering difficulties crossing the Flow Country. This land is flat, bounded by mountains on the south and west. It gradually slopes down to the coast in the north and east. It is a scene of brown moss with patches of green indicating treacherous peat bog. Anything larger than a bird might sink.

The *Inverness Courier* reported that the track was laid by scooping out three or four feet of moss. Turf was then laid in the bottom as a foundation and packed with gravel and sand to form a roadway. Horses and carts brought materials along the trench as there were no roads in the district. It is possible that this method was used in the building of parts of the Slamamman Railway and that William passed on the information.

Forsinard Station, seen in 2009, is now unstaffed, like all the other stations on the line. However, the stone building has found a new use as a visitor centre for the Royal Society for the Protection of Birds. Just south of this lonely station in the Flow Country is an area notorious for snow drifts. (Keith Fenwick)

William Roberts was appointed as the resident engineer. His father, also William, was Superintendent of the Line for the Highland Railway. The latter retired in 1874 due to ill health and took up farming at Dell of Inshes, the old Paterson farm.

Building a railway in a sparsely inhabited area has its problems for the personnel doing the work. The workers lived in barrack accommodation for about sixty people. Newspapers reported that they were roomy and well furnished. When work was finished for the day, a train went along the line picking up the men and transporting them to their quarters. The area is renowned for snow particularly to the south of Forsinard, nicknamed in our household as "frozen hard." Murdoch by all accounts was a great leader of men and was not afraid to take off his jacket and work with the men himself. In 1869, just a few years earlier, there was a gold rush in the Kildonan area so perhaps the men amused themselves in the summer panning for gold in the river, imagining they might make their fortunes.

As well as laying the track Murdoch had to think about the terminal stations at Wick and Thurso. Before Telford arrived to carry out the harbour improvements under the British Fisheries Society, an old wooden bridge supported on stone pillars was the only crossing of the Wick River. Eighteenth century Wick was a small village on the north side of the river. After the harbour improvements Wick became a centre for the herring fishing industry and in the nineteenth century was one of the largest herring fishing ports in Europe.

Telford also planned an adjacent town on the south side of the river linked to the old village by a new stone bridge that he designed. He called this area Pulteneytown, after Sir William Pulteney, Governor of the British Fisheries Society. By the time of the coming of the railway, it was felt that a wider flatter bridge was required. Telford's bridge had a carriageway of only fifteen feet. Who better to ask to design the bridge than Murdoch, the engineer who was bringing a railway to two far-flung

Wick Station in Highland Railway days. The harbour is beyond the railway, down a short hill. Thurso station building is of similar design.   *(Highland Railway Society/Roberts collection)*

Murdoch Paterson's bridge at Wick, which replaced Telford's bridge.   *(Anne-Mary Paterson)*

towns in the extreme north of Scotland? The bridge, like Telford's, has three segmental arches with spans of forty-eight, sixty and forty feet. His designs for the stations at both Thurso and Wick are very similar and like most at the end of a major line, had roofs over the platforms.

Work complete and inspected, the whole line from Helmsdale to Wick and Thurso opened to great excitement on 28th July 1874. The inhabitants of the towns on the northern outpost of Britain could now travel by rail to London and further afield.

Murdoch's son Donald was now a grown man. Information about him is very sketchy except that he was an assistant engineer on the Highland Railway, so it must have been about this time that he left school and started an apprenticeship to become a civil engineer.

After the railway opened in 1874, Murdoch took his daughter Elizabeth for an outing to Wick, which then took most of the day. In an 1885 timetable, a train left Inverness at nine in the morning and arrived in Wick at five in the afternoon. There were of course many more stations than there are now so the train stopped many times. Before the motor car, passengers might just travel short distances from one station to another. An example is at Culrain Station to the west of the river Oykel. The next stop is Invershin on the east bank half a mile away; the rail bridge is the only connection between the two.

While Murdoch was going about his business, probably to do with the bridge at Wick, Elizabeth wandered off to explore the town. At the harbour, a man, William Murray, was preaching and evangelising to any of the religious fisherfolk who cared to listen. He was a member of the Christian Brethren Church and came from Glasgow. For some reason, he and Elizabeth spoke to one another. There must have been a mutual attraction as a romance started. It would seem they had secret assignations in Inverness to get to know one another better. After a while, Murdoch found out about this liaison. He would naturally have expected his only daughter to marry someone better able to support her. William Murray was the illegitimate son of Helen Watson, a retired domestic cook. He worked as a merchants' clerk.

When Murdoch discovered the romance, Elizabeth announced she wanted to marry William. The family story goes that she eloped to Beauly where a relation of her mother lived. They arranged to get married there. Just at the point when the minister was asking if there was any reason why the couple should not get married, Murdoch burst into the church saying that he forbad the marriage. Of course, there was no reason why two single adults who were both of age could not get married. Much to Murdoch's relief because of his unexpected interruption, the minister abandoned the service to look further into the matter. After this disaster Elizabeth, who seems to have been a determined woman, decided not to return home and took a job as a domestic servant in Beauly. It is of course possible that she did not get on with her stepmother and no longer wished to live in the parental home.

Towards the end of 1874 Peter Wilson, the Highland Railway engineer, took ill and was unable to work. On 1st December, the post was offered to Murdoch on a temporary basis until 1st July 1875. Being self-employed, he must have been pleased about this offer which he accepted as most of his work on the line to Caithness was finished. Peter Wilson died on 31st December.

Frances, Murdoch's wife, was pregnant. They were married at least four years by this time. People did not speak about such matters so it is not recorded whether Frances had difficulty conceiving or whether she suffered miscarriages but their first child, Violet Mary Jane, was born in Kensington, London on 1st February 1875. At thirty-seven Frances was old in those days to be having her first baby. Maybe her parents felt that she would have a safer, more comfortable confinement in London. Childbirth was a dangerous affair. Murdoch was well aware of this remembering that Jane, his brother James' wife, died at the age of twenty-one after the birth of Donald.

Around 1875 the town fathers of Inverness decided the water supply needed attention. The existing system, which pumped water from the river Ness up to a holding tank at Drummond on the hill above the town, was totally inadequate. The pump worked off a water wheel in the river Ness. In very wet or very dry weather the wheel did not turn properly. As early as 1864 Joseph Mitchell, who lived at Viewhill near to the holding tank, had said that Loch Ashie, in the hills to the south, would make an excellent reservoir for the water supply. Joseph suggested that the Inverness Gas & Water Commissioners seek the help of W. Bateman, an eminent London engineer, to do a survey and report on the suitability of Loch Ashie or the nearby Loch Dunchelchaig that some other people had suggested. Mr Bateman said that Loch Ashie would be very suitable but the water level would require raising with a dam. Mr Bateman was often away on other business so the commissioners suggested that Murdoch draw up the plans for the water supply. Mr Bateman approved them and work started in October 1875.

Murdoch's period as acting engineer to the Highland Railway ended on 30th June 1875. The post was then offered to him on a permanent basis at a salary of £600 per annum. He could finish his work on the waterworks but he was then supposed to devote his whole working time to the Highland Railway. He was elected a member of the Institution of Civil Engineers and so began a new, and perhaps the greatest, chapter of Murdoch's life.

END OF A PARTNERSHIP

The latter part of the 1870s, with so many lines opened, was a period of consolidation and improvements to stations, track and signalling systems. Murdoch, as engineer to the Highland Railway was responsible for the line from Stanley Junction to as far north as Bonar Bridge and eastwards to Keith. The other lines belonged to the respective companies who had built them, but were worked by the Highland Railway under financial arrangements which included their maintenance, so Murdoch was responsible for them as well. He must have had a deep knowledge of all the lines, as he had been involved in the surveying and building of most of them. People always described him as a kindly man who knew most of his staff by name. He was also very conscientious about his work and by his example appears to have been a leader of men. Part of his daily apparel was a walking stick, which he always carried at half cock even into his later life, but presumably it had a variety of other uses.

In January 1876, Elizabeth and William Murray married at Pollockshaws, Glasgow in the Christian Brethren Church in Cogan Street. Elizabeth's occupation in the register is a domestic worker in Beauly. The address given is 7 Carfin Street, Crosshill, Glasgow. In the following November Elizabeth gave birth to their first child, a son. In spite of all the problems with her father, they named him Murdoch Paterson. They were still living in Crosshill, but at 8 Hilton Terrace. There were to be two more children, Elena Jane and Violet Elizabeth. Both were born in Australia. So it must have been soon after Murdoch's birth that the other Murdoch heard that they were considering emigrating. Murdoch agreed to pay their fares. Unfortunately, the ship had some sort of problem and they returned to England so Murdoch had to buy them new passages. Happily, this time they arrived safely in Melbourne where the family settled. His concern over her marriage shows that Murdoch was obviously fond of Elizabeth. It must have been a wrench for him to see her off to Australia knowing that he would never see her or his grandchildren again. But at the same time he was rid of a son-in-law of whom he disapproved and he may well have thought that William could give Elizabeth a better life in Australia.

With a secure job Murdoch and Frances moved to a grander home at 13 Ness Bank on the town side of the river. On 8th April 1878 Frances, now aged forty gave birth to their second child, Murdoch William, this time at home in Inverness.

Death was never far round the corner in those days and at the end of September 1880, Murdoch William took ill with a fever. He died on 14th October, probably from a form of meningitis.

Queen Victoria spent most of the summer and autumn at Balmoral and all things Scottish and Highland were fashionable. She used the Inverness & Perth Junction Railway as early as September 1863 to visit the Duke of Atholl at Blair Castle when he was dying of cancer; she used it several times on later visits to the Highlands. Fortunes made in industry meant that various wealthy people and members of the aristocracy bought estates in the Highlands. They travelled by train with house parties in the "season," August and September, to their "shooting lodges" as they called their Scottish properties. The men of the parties shot grouse, went deerstalking, and attended balls with their partners. Several of the landowners were directors of the railway and they and the other proprietors could use the railway as well for exporting timber, whisky, agricultural products and fish from their estates; consequently the value of their land increased.

In 1878 there was a new Act concerning roads and bridges in Scotland, so William Paterson in his capacity as a consultant engineer was asked to prepare a list of the state of the highways in the various districts for presentation to a meeting in April 1879. Later that year, in October, the Committee overseeing roads in Inverness-shire formally appointed William as consulting engineer. This probably involved doing a thorough survey but William, having dealt with the roads for many years, was an obvious candidate for the post. He was by all accounts a very conscientious though quiet man, so by 1880 he was busy identifying problems. By this time he was sixty-eight years of age, old by modern standards to take up a new appointment. One problem in particular was the bridge over the river Findhorn at Tomatin which required to be renewed. By October 1880, William had the plans ready for the Committee.

Around this time his wife Janet was visiting Margaret their daughter and her husband, John Arres–Mather, who was now farming at Delnies near Nairn. On 5th October, she took ill and became paralysed presumably from a stroke. She died on 12th October aged seventy-one. She and William had been married for forty-one years. It is recorded that William, ever hardworking and reliable, was at a highways meeting on 10th October to report on Garramore Bridge over the river Spey which he said was in the thorough state of repair so it could be adopted by the Badenoch District of Inverness-shire.

He was back at meetings by 18th October with his plans and specifications for the Tomatin Bridge. Major Bruce, who was in charge of the 1920s reconstruction of the A9, photographed the bridge which showed that it was a two span metal truss bridge. In November, Oliver & Arrol were appointed contractors. It is not recorded when work started on the bridge. William supervised this and issued progress certificates.

The Highland Railway was planning the first line on its own account, a modest thirteen and three quarter miles from Keith to Buckie and Portessie serving six stations. William was assisting Murdoch, probably in a consulting capacity, with the surveys and plans for the line. It did not involve great engineering work. The line was authorised in June 1882 and opened in August 1884.

Clearing snow by hand.   *(Highland Railway Society/Roberts collection)*

An Engineer's Train near Newtonmore in 1923. Murdoch would have used a similar train, but with older locomotives and rolling stock, for his 'snowblock special' and other jobs he took part in.   (J L Stevenson colln)

Murdoch is remembered for rescuing trains caught in snowdrifts. John Edgar Campbell recollected the following of Murdoch in *Iron Track Through the Highlands* :

'It was perhaps at the snowblocks – and there were SOME snowblocks in those days – that Mr Paterson was at his best. He was a born general, and knew how to take the most out of men without assuming the role of a slave driver. He, on such occasions, made himself one of themselves and his directions were usually in such language as "we'll do this boys or we'll do that…." His "shovel brigade" always did what he asked them to do. He had a rail carriage called the "snowblock special" from which refreshments were dispensed to all involved, including whisky, usually from the distillery at Clynish, Brora in Sutherland.'

The winter of 1880-81 was bad. In December 1880 two trains, one travelling north and another south, became snowbound on either side of Dava Station between Grantown-on-Spey and Forres. The passengers evacuated both trains but the northbound train also had trucks with cattle. Mixed trains were common on the Highland. The cattle refused to leave the trucks so as the blizzard built up snow around the train they suffocated. Wreaths of it blew up to over twenty feet. The station staff at Dava had to crawl through improvised tunnels to get in and out of the buildings. Pilot engines with snowploughs left Inverness but the snow was so deep they could not break through. The idea was that the engine charged the drift at full speed. Huge blocks of snow flew into the air, sometimes fifty feet high falling to the ground with a dull thud.

Murdoch and a squad of men hastily departed on the "snowblock special." On arrival at the north side, the shovel brigade set to work. They worked in tiers passing the snow upwards as they cleared the line. It was very hard exhausting work so the "special" dispensed frequent refreshments. Dava Station had been isolated for five days when Murdoch and his men broke through. He was so worried about the possible loss of human life that he was speechless with relief when he found that the passengers and the staff from the train were safe, though rather hungry.

In January 1881, there were deep drifts north of Helmsdale, again at Dava and at Druimuachdar.

On 22nd January, snow completely cut off Inverness. It was busy winter.

At the beginning of May 1881, William suddenly took ill. He had some sort of cellular skin infection that affected his neck and chest. With no antibiotics in those days, this probably led to blood poisoning. The obituary records that there was no hope of his recovery from the very beginning. He died at his home, Larkfield, Southside Road, Inverness on 29th May.

Who was to continue with supervising the work at the bridge at Tomatin? On 14th June, the Roads Committee asked the clerk to find another engineer. Later in the month, William Roberts applied. He had been Murdoch's resident engineer during the building of the railway in Caithness and was now in practice in Kingussie. However, the highways committee was cautious and took some time to make a decision. When they finally decided to appoint Mr Roberts they asked Murdoch to conduct a watching brief on his late brother's behalf. William Roberts may not have realised it at the time but this further contact

William Roberts, Murdoch's trusted assistant and then Highland Railway engineer after Murdoch's death. (Highland Railway Society/Roberts collection)

with Murdoch was to prove the starting point of a new engineering career for him.

By October, Murdoch reported that the bridge was complete to his and William Roberts' satisfaction and that the contractors should be given their final payment. The bridge was replaced again in 1926 with a concrete double span bridge.

If it had not been for his brother William, would Murdoch have become a civil engineer? Would Joseph Mitchell have been able to build the railways in the Highlands without William's and then Murdoch's assistance? Without William, the railways in the Highlands might have been very different. Joseph had the vision and the ability to find financial backers to build the railway, but it was William who probably made it a reality using his experience of surveying, planning and building railways gained under Sir John McNeill. No doubt the Great North of Scotland Railway would eventually have found enough money to reach Inverness but their route to the south was not through Druimuachdar to Perth. Others, such as the Caledonian Railway, might have built that later.

William, an elder of the Old High Kirk in Inverness, seems to have been a quiet man going about his business conscientiously. Murdoch, usually known as Murdo, was on the other hand more of an extrovert. He often greeted his workers, "Well how are you getting on boddach?" By the word "boddach" he probably meant "man." This might suggest that he knew their faces but not their names. It is doubtful whether he and William used Gaelic as an everyday language. They must have had some knowledge of it because many of the workers would have come from the crofting areas cleared for sheep grazing where they spoke Gaelic.

Together, along with Joseph Mitchell, William and Murdoch changed the face of transport in the Highlands. No longer had travellers to face bumpy rides in stagecoaches or long stormy sea voyages. These improvements brought about the establishment of new whisky distilleries, many of which were located beside the railway. Fish, meat and other products could be sent promptly to markets in the south. All this brought about increasing prosperity in the North of Scotland.

COMPLETION OF THE DREAM

The Highland Railway was happy to continue with the status quo although their route to the south at that time was rather longer than necessary. It did serve areas of population along the coast to Forres and then south to Grantown-on-Spey before reaching Aviemore. A shorter route over the hills between Inverness and Aviemore would mean lower fares and therefore less income. However, an unwelcome competitor arrived proposing to build a railway from Glasgow to Inverness via Fort William and the Great Glen. A parliamentary committee considered this bill in May 1883. The Highland Railway representative gave evidence showing that there were engineering problems. He also said that the Company was proposing a more direct route to Inverness as a counter to the bill.

While the shorter line was under consideration, Joseph Mitchell died at his home in London on 26th November 1883. Although not always the easiest man to get on with, he had the vision and the connections to find the money and backing to build railways in the Highlands. He and William had groomed Murdoch and given him a practical training in building railways. The three men made a good partnership.

Murdoch must have wondered if the direct route to Aviemore was even possible. It passed through wild uninhabited country, had to cross two river valleys, the Findhorn and the Nairn, and the summit at Slochd was nearly as high as Druimuachdar. It is cauldron shaped and the approaches especially from the south are much narrower and steeper.

Murdoch probably started making a preliminary assessment in the early 1880s. Murdoch

Slochd Viaduct, just south of the summit, was part of the solution for avoiding a tunnel under the highest part of the line. Here, a southbound sleeper for London crosses the viaduct in 1931.   (H C Casserley, per H Hesling)

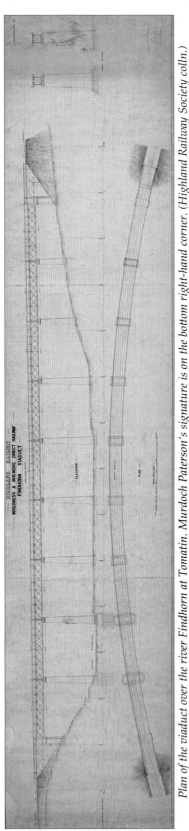

Plan of the viaduct over the river Findhorn at Tomatin. Murdoch Paterson's signature is on the bottom right-hand corner. (Highland Railway Society colln.)

MacDonald (later Sir Murdoch) who began as an apprentice on the Highland Railway in 1884, recalled in a letter to the *Inverness Courier* that Murdoch Paterson had told him that he thought that the only way to cross Slochd was by a tunnel to the east of the pass. The directors of the Highland Railway were not keen on this extra expense. One Sunday morning Murdoch, as this subject was much on his mind, had a sudden inspiration that it might just be possible to build a railway to the west without a tunnel. As it was the Sabbath Day, he had to wait on tenterhooks until Monday morning before he could go to the office to examine his plans and instruct the surveyors to look into his idea. The route proved to be achievable so one hurdle was out of the way.

The directors must have been concerned about the engineering complexities of the line because they appointed John Fowler as consulting engineer. How much input he had into the design is not known. He may just have been someone to whom Murdoch could refer if he wanted an opinion. John Fowler was now a successful London civil engineer so was busy with other work, unlike the period just after his return from abroad when he had time to interfere with the design of the railway to Strome.

The Highland Railway Minutes of 2nd January 1884 state that Fowler persuaded the directors to approve a route crossing the river Findhorn by a huge viaduct, saving one and a half miles on the journey. Presumably the longer route involved a more modest crossing of the river to the south of the village of Tomatin near the road bridge that was being rebuilt when William died.

The Highland's plans for the direct line were ready for submission to Parliament in the 1883-4 session. There were still competing proposals; one from the Great North of Scotland for a line from Boat of Garten to Inverness and another from a different company for a line from Cambus o'May on Deeside, Aberdeenshire, to Nethy Bridge but the parliamentary committee decided for the Highland Railway in July 1884. At the same time, it approved a short branch line to Strathpeffer starting at Fodderty just beyond Dingwall on the Strome line.

Strathpeffer was becoming more popular as a spa. Visitors, especially if they were disabled or invalids, found the steep carriage drive from Achterneed very difficult and trying. Therefore, the demand was there for a branch line. The two and a half miles from just outside Dingwall did not pose difficult engineering, the steepest gradient being one in one hundred. A bit of waste ground near Fodderty, a village along the route, had ballast suitable for making the track bed.

In those days, civil engineers in remote parts had to be

Close-up view of the viaduct over the river Findhorn near Tomatin. *(I D C Wharton)*

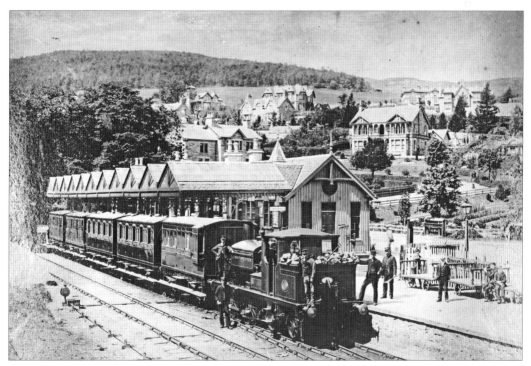

Strathpeffer station with a train for Dingwall hauled by the eponymous locomotive, a Stroudley 0-4-4T. Although the building is still in use, this view is now impossible due to the growth of trees.

(Highland Railway Society)

Nairn was one of the rebuilt stations for which Murdoch Paterson was responsible. It was re-constructed in 1885.The stone building consisted of one long central section supporting an awning for passenger protection with two gabled sections at right angles at each end.   *(Keith Fenwick)*

architects as well. Murdoch designed a splendid station described in *The Buildings of Scotland* as a "picturesque wooden building, the deep, gableted glass-and-wood awning over the platform supported by cast iron columns." Visitors must have had a good impression of the place when they arrived. The Board of Trade inspection was on 2nd June 1885 and the line opened to the public on 3rd June. Sadly, the line is now closed but the station was completely renovated a number of years ago and is now a picturesque visitor centre and shops.

By the 1880s, some new stone station buildings were built with better staff and passenger facilities as some of the early ones had been hastily constructed. Although Murdoch had overall responsibility and *Buildings of Scotland* credits him as architect for Dingwall and Nairn, it is known that George Craig, an assistant, was involved in the design of Nairn. Similar styles were used for the rebuilding of Pitlochry, Newtonmore and Brora.

In March 1885 Donald, Murdoch's son by his first marriage, was an assistant engineer in the Highland Railway. He took ill with phthisis, then a name often used for tuberculosis. Violet, their daughter was just ten at this time and having lost other children, Murdoch and Frances were probably anxious in case she contracted the disease and that her half brother's illness might distress her. Donald went to stay at Dysart Cottages, Moulin near Pitlochry. Perhaps the woman of the house was some kind of nurse or maybe Murdoch knew of her because her husband worked on the railway. A Dr Irvine looked after Donald. He died aged thirty on 21st November 1885 at two o'clock in the morning. The end may have been sudden because Murdoch was not present. Donald was buried beside his mother, Jane, in the Chapel Yard, Inverness. The description on the tombstone says he was Murdoch and Jane's "only and beloved son" and that "His end was in peace." Was his illness one of much suffering? We shall never know.

The Highland Railway was in no hurry to build the direct line from Aviemore to Inverness as it passed through areas which at that time were either uninhabited or had small populations. It also involved heavy engineering that required fine-tuning so some areas required resurveying in order to produce working drawings. The owners and tenants of the land through which the railway would pass needed contacting in order to negotiate purchase. Many of the landowners supported the railway and readily agreed to the acquisition of the land required, sometimes free of charge. The Mackintosh of Mackintosh was understandably not very happy about a level crossing on the drive to his home, Moy Hall, so the railway agreed to a bridge. They also provided him with a stone built station. Most other stations were wooden.

The principal objector was Duncan Forbes of Culloden who lived at Culloden House. The land to the south of Inverness is steep. The original plan was for the track to branch off the Elgin line a few miles east of Inverness and rise slowly across the slope up to the summit above the valley of the river Nairn in a cutting some seventy feet deep. A considerable viaduct was required to span the river. However, Forbes was not happy as it was too near his residence.

A deviation was put to Parliament in May 1887 with a new line that left the existing line at Millburn, just to the east of Inverness Station. It then climbs at gradients of one in sixty and one in seventy in a big sweep across the hillside, passing near the site of the Battle of Culloden. It curves up to the summit where it goes underneath a road and enters Culloden Moor Station, now closed. It then continues across the very large stone viaduct over the river Nairn and shortly joins the route as originally planned.

The easiest section of the line was from Aviemore to Carr Bridge. In December 1889 John Ross & Son, a company from Fearn in Easter Ross, was given the contract. In September 1890, the next section to the river Findhorn was awarded to Hugh Kennedy & Son. This was the difficult section over Slochd Summit, at 1,315ft the second highest summit on the Highland. If you travel southward along the modern A9 road, just south of the pass itself the railway is above you on the right. After what seems only a short distance the road crosses the railway and it is far below in a cutting. The rock cutting at the summit itself is 65ft deep and involved excavating three hundred and fifty thousand cubic yards of rock and waste. To the south just before it passes under the A9 is the eight arch stone Slochd viaduct, one hundred and five feet high and four hundred feet long. Along this section are

Slochd viaduct in the 1930s. The old A9 is in the foreground. Slochd summit is to the right and the line heads off to the left towards Carr Bridge in a deep cutting. The modern A9 is behind the camera.   (From a postcard)

Tomatin Viaduct under construction (above) and complete (below). Wooden staging was used to support the arches during construction. The road underneath is the old A9. This stone viaduct is to the north of the much longer steel trussed viaduct over the river Findhorn illustrated on pages 52 and 53.

(Highland Railway Society/Roberts collection)

steep gradients, sometimes one in sixty.

As the line continues northwards from Slochd it drops down to Tomatin where it crosses the Findhorn on the deviation suggested by John Fowler. This viaduct, illustrated on pages 52 and 53, has an elegant curving half-mile radius. It is four hundred and forty feet long with nine double triangulated steel truss spans of one hundred and thirty two feet supported on slender masonry piers, the highest being one hundred and forty four feet. After a short embankment, the line then crosses a dry valley on a very different viaduct of nine stone arches with narrow slightly splayfooted piers and brick vaults, illustrated opposite. The two viaducts were a separate contract but together this section was a massive engineering undertaking for those times, even allowing for the introduction of some mechanisation such as steam cranes.

There were short branch lines to think about as well. In 1861 a branch to Burghead from Alves between Elgin and Forres on the Aberdeen line was opened. The Highland decided to extend this line two miles to Hopeman, probably because the Great North of Scotland was showing an interest in this place. The stone quarry at Cummingstown, half a mile before Hopeman, provided opportunities for freight and passengers.

Fort George, an army barracks built after the Jacobite uprisings to house troops to subdue the "wild" Highlanders, had a station of this name on the Inverness to Aberdeen line. It was rather a long way from the Fort, so a branch line of one and a half miles was built to Ardersier, the nearest village. The old station was renamed Gollanfield Junction. Neither of these involved great engineering works.

Between the Inverness and Cromarty Firths lies an area known as the Black Isle, not a real island but in the nineteenth century an isolated fertile peninsula. It has fishing villages like Avoch and Fortrose on the south coast and a thriving agricultural economy that badly needed better transport. The nearest railway station was Muir of Ord, about thirteen miles from Fortrose, so the proposal was for a railway line to Rosemarkie about a mile east of Fortrose. In the event it only reached as far as Fortrose but this became a busy station with a siding for loading cattle on to special trucks and for other

goods. Sandstone quarries, now all closed, provided another source of traffic, along with fish and other agricultural products such as potatoes and barley. Coal and lime for fertilising the land were delivered to the stations. Passengers had to transfer to the main line at

Laying the keystone of the bridge over Munlochy Burn on the Black Isle branch, 24 June 1892. In earlier days, embankments of this size were avoided if possible.
(Alasdair Cameron collection)

Muir of Ord. No great engineering was needed for this line either as it followed the fairly flat coast. All three branches received parliamentary approval in July 1890. John Ross & Son won the contract for the Black Isle line and work started in November of that year. The resident engineer in charge of the construction was Murdoch MacDonald who had now completed his apprenticeship. The line opened in February 1894. Murdoch MacDonald continued working for the railway until sometime between 1896 and 1898. He was later to achieve great eminence in the civil engineering profession (see the Epilogue).

The Crown area on the hill above Inverness was becoming the fashionable place to live so Murdoch and family moved about this time to Crown Villa in what was then Victoria Circus, now known as Crown Circus. It would have been much more convenient for him than his previous house in Ness Bank as the area is on the hill right above Inverness Station.

Ullapool was one of three fishing villages established by the British Fisheries Society during Telford's time. There was an oversupply of fish there which it was felt could be sold in the south and in England where it was becoming a more popular food. Moves were afoot to replace the existing rough track by building a railway from Garve, a station on the line to Strome Ferry.

Murdoch must have done a rough survey of the line because on 16th April 1889 he accompanied James Caldwell, Member of Parliament for St.Rollox in Glasgow, and his daughter to a public meeting in Ullapool to discuss the railway. After Mr Caldwell spoke, Murdoch told the assembled people of Ullapool the approximate line that the railway would take. During the summer, Mr C R Manners, a civil engineer in practice in Inverness, carried out a fuller survey.

The railway was to pass through bleak and, in winter, cold countryside, sometimes at gradients of one in forty up the valley of the Blackwater to Aultguish Inn. There was then a climb over the Diridh Mor summit at nine hundred and three feet to descend to Corrieshalloch Gorge. This was a severe obstacle but Murdoch had already solved the problem of Slochd so he was not going to be beaten by this one!

This gorge is a relic of the Ice Age when a glacier flowed from the Pass of the Diridh Mor to the Atlantic. When the ice started melting 10–13,000 years ago, water roared down to what is now Loch Broom on which Ullapool is situated. It cut a gorge with sheer walls about a mile long due to local fractures in the rock. It is one hundred feet wide and one hundred and fifty feet deep. The Falls of Measach on the river Droma drop one hundred and fifty feet into the gorge at its head.

The only possible way through this area was to bring the track down on the southwest side of the gorge almost to where the river Cuileig joins the Droma to become the river Broom. It would then form a sort of "U" shape by proceeding alongside the Cuileg for about three quarters of a mile, cross the river, proceed along the opposite bank, and then enter a tunnel of five hundred and ninety yards with gradients along this section of one in forty for about two and a half miles. The river Broom flows into the head of Loch Broom, one of the longest sea lochs on the west coast of Scotland. Ullapool is about twelve miles from Corrieshalloch. The hillside by the loch falls steeply into the sea making further difficulties. Along the route before there were in parts more gradients of one in forty.

Sir John Fowler's estate at Braemore included the gorge so he was very keen on the railway. He was busy with his partner Sir Benjamin Baker on other activities, notably the Forth Railway Bridge, so he could not devote much time to the project. His son John Arthur was on the committee promoting the railway. In 1867, not long after his acquisition of the estate, John Fowler built a beautiful suspension bridge over the Corrieshalloch Gorge above the falls. The National Trust for Scotland now owns the area and the bridge provides a splendid viewing point for those not afraid of its dizzy height. Sir John also built an impressive mansion house, Braemore Lodge, which had one of the earliest hydroelectric schemes to supply power to the house and outbuildings. He also designed two other footbridges.

The Garve and Ullapool Railway received parliamentary approval during the 1890 session. It was never constructed as a Treasury subsidy could not be obtained because a government commission was set up to consider where there should be railways from Inverness to the west coast. Sadly, it favoured other lines: one to the Gairloch area that Murdoch is also said to have surveyed and another to somewhere north of Lochinver. The ferry from Stornoway, Isle of Lewis, now uses Ullapool as its port so passengers and freight have to travel by road to Inverness. Would this interesting railway, if constructed, have become another "great train journey of the world" like its counterpart to Kyle of Lochalsh?

Murdoch had other important things to think about, such as finding out how much the viaducts over the rivers Nairn and Findhorn would cost, so that the Highland Railway Board could approve their design. Sir John Fowler, as consulting engineer, no doubt had contacts. His experience with the Forth Railway Bridge was useful in the design of the Findhorn Viaduct which included steelwork. He was a busy man and it is generally considered that Murdoch was the designer of the viaducts, even though Fowler's name is on the plates of both the Findhorn and Nairn viaducts. Sir John was, as we have seen, a great supporter of the Highland Railway and probably a very useful source for advice.

In 1890, Murdoch's energetic life was catching up with him. In those days with no proper protective clothing to keep out the elements, he must often have been cold and soaking wet. As well as the day-to-day tasks of maintaining the existing tracks and signalling, which included dealing with snow blocks and floods, he now had the heavy responsibility of designing and superintending the construction of the new lines. It was all a bit much for a man now aged sixty-five, so in October 1891 he asked the Directors if he could have an assistant. They appointed William Roberts, who had taken over superintending the construction of the road bridge at Tomatin when William Paterson died, and who was still in business in Kingussie. Murdoch probably suggested him, as he knew him from the Caithness and Sutherland Railway days; afterwards he had worked on railways in India. Murdoch was now just responsible for new lines.

What the Highland Railway directors really wanted to do was to extend the line from Strome Ferry to what is now Kyle of Lochalsh. Murdoch knew that though this stretch was only ten and a half miles long it was as challenging a task as the Aviemore to Inverness direct line. The track had to wind along a steep rocky coast which involved blasting cuttings through very hard rock.

Meanwhile Murdoch was superintending the direct line from Aviemore. The first section to Carr Bridge, built by John Ross, opened in July 1892 as a branch line. John Ross' diaries of this period are still in existence and they show that he had very regular contact and a growing friendship with Murdoch

Rock cutting near Kyle of Lochalsh. Spectacular blasting was needed to build this line. (Highland Railway Society/ Roberts collection)

Building the direct line from Aviemore required the reconstruction of the station there, which developed from a simple wayside stop to a major junction with provision for splitting and joining trains, marshalling wagons and servicing locomotives. The large new station building is seen under construction with the old, ramshackle looking wooden building beyond it.   *(Highland Railway Society colln.)*

Such is the size of the Nairn Viaduct at Culloden that it is difficult to photograph the whole structure. This view from a postcard was taken from the east and shows how it dominates the landscape.

though he always referred to him as Mr Paterson. John Ross was not a young man either. He lived near Tain in Easter Ross. First he would travel to the Black Isle to view the work on the new line there; then over Kessock Ferry and up to Carr Bridge, all one assumes by horse drawn trap or something similar. This was in all seasons. He must have been good at his railway work and found it profitable for he won the contract in December 1891 for the section from the river Findhorn to Culdoich, south of Culloden. At least this was a bit nearer Inverness. In October 1892, Mackay & Mackay took over the last section to Inverness, including the massive stone viaduct over the river Nairn.

In the summer of 1892, the Highland Railway decided that it would definitely extend the line from Strome Ferry to Kyle of Lochalsh provided the government said it would not approve any other lines to the west coast. The application to Parliament in 1893 included a pier at Kyle for fishing vessels and shipping from the Outer and Inner Hebrides. The railway from Strome winds along Loch Carron below the steep hillside passing Alexander Matheson's residence at Duncraig Castle. Just past this is Plockton station that for reasons of topography is three quarters of a mile away from the village which had expanded when it became a settlement for victims of the Clearances earlier in the nineteenth century. The line then curves round to the southwest, past the crofting villages of Duirinish and Drumbuie, before sweeping over the bay in front of Erbusaig. The first plan for the next stretch past there was for a tunnel one hundred and fifty yards long, but in the end, they decided to make it a deep cutting. Further rock cutting was required to reach the village of Kyle itself. Parliament approved the extension in June 1893. The government then offered a subsidy for the railway from Fort William to Mallaig. This probably killed off any proposals for the Garve to Ullapool and the Achnasheen to Gairloch Railways.

By mid August an advertisement appeared inviting tenders for the Kyle extension. The first tender was for three hundred and eighty thousand cubic yards of rock cutting, one hundred and twenty cubic yards of soft excavation, forty seven culverts and bridges varying from four to thirty feet plus rail laying, ballasting and erection of stations. The second for the construction of the pier required one hundred and ten thousand cubic yards of rock excavation and ninety five thousand cubic yards of rock filling and concrete work as well as platforms, loading areas, and so on. On 6th September, both contracts were let to John Best & Sons of Edinburgh, experienced contractors in the construction of railways and harbours.

Work started in early October. There were fifty men by the end of October, mostly locals because huts had not yet been built to accommodate workers. A brick magazine was needed near Erbusaig to house the explosives for blasting the cuttings. Unfortunately, that winter was very wet, so when Murdoch presented his report in April 1894, he said that there had been very little progress although

Duirinish, on the extension from Strome Ferry to Kyle of Lochalsh. When photographed in 1954, it was little changed from the time of opening, with a simple building reflecting the limited demand in such a sparsely populated area.

(J L Stevenson)

three hundred and eighty men were by then on the job, preparing the new pier and building bridges. By September, the Ross-shire Journal reported that four and a half miles had been cut.

Although Murdoch's health was still failing, he was entering what must have been the busiest years of his professional life. Victorian civil engineers constructed projects for posterity and wished to leave behind quality work. Some may say it was a sort of vanity so that they would be remembered, the bigger and more spectacular the better. However, they also had a responsibility for people's lives. They had to build track, bridges and tunnels that were properly

Achanor, Murdoch's last home on Crown Drive, Inverness as it is today. It was built in the 1890s so he and his family would have been the first occupants.   *(Anne-Mary Paterson)*

designed and constructed, particularly after the Tay Bridge disaster of 1879. They were leaving behind something useful for future generations.

In the early 1890s, Murdoch and his family moved again to what was to be their final home, Achanor (Gaelic for "Field of Gold"). It was in the same area as Crown Villa so he would have prior knowledge of it, and most probably he was the first owner. It was a property regarded as suitable by the Victorian standards of the day for a man of his growing stature in Inverness and the Highlands.

A parade of navvies photographed at the Findhorn Viaduct, Tomatin, during the excursion of July 1894. Murdoch was not present.   *(J L Stevenson collection)*

Maybe too his wife remembering London aspired to something grand.

Murdoch was supervising projects miles apart but at least he could travel most of the way by train to the works on the Kyle line. The Black Isle line was much nearer with supervision in the capable hands of his former apprentice Murdoch MacDonald. The direct line from Aviemore was progressing slowly, so great were the engineering works.

John Ross' diaries show that Murdoch regularly visited the work even though there were resident engineers on each of the sections. Although there was already a railway from the south to Inverness, the spectacular nature of the new line caused quite a stir in the public imagination. John Ross organised an excursion on 4th July 1894 to view the construction of the viaduct over the Findhorn. Although he had the contract from there, the masonry and steelwork for the viaduct were separate contracts.

The expedition left from Inverness. It must have been quite a sight because a large and powerful traction engine with a whistling mechanism specially fitted for the occasion pulled two wagons for the passengers and a brake van. The occasion seems to have been a jolly and noisy affair with refreshment stops, no doubt alcoholic, as they progressed along the road. Murdoch was not present at the event but *The Scottish Highlander* describes what the visitors saw : 'The peaceful river, out of which the massive pillars which form the masonry seem to grow, the many and various puffing and snorting steam engines, the hundreds of navvies, and the beautiful green herbage of the Highland glen present a picture which will remain in the mind's eye of the fortunate spectator for a lifetime.'

In a lecture to the Inverness Field Club in 1897 Mr D J Reid, an assistant engineer on the Daviot to Millburn section, said that machinery replaced brawn. This was not entirely true but on the Kyle line the average age of the workers was higher than on earlier jobs. On 13th June 1895 John Ross records that Murdoch and Sir John Fowler were at the Findhorn Viaduct and a man came from Glasgow to put up a steam crane, presumably for erecting the steel work. The crane took five days to be ready. In July, military engineers visited the viaduct.

During this time, John Ross and Murdoch went together to the Altnaslanach Bridge at Moy a few miles north of the Findhorn. The ground around was so boggy that foundations could not be found so Murdoch built it of green-heart wood to give it strength. It is one hundred and forty seven

Altnaslanach Bridge near Moy. This was built of wood because of the soft ground and was the only wooden railway bridge left in Britain until it was renovated early in the 21st century. As with many Gaelic names, there are different spellings, e.g. Allt-na-Slanach as used by Professor Paxton in his Foreward to this book.

(Highland Railway Society)

feet long and has five spans of eight yards width. Gillian Nelson describes it in *Highland Bridges* as looking like a piece of wooden Mecanno when viewed sideways. This type of bridge was common on railways in parts of America where there was plenty of wood but little stone and in many cases they were a great deal bigger. Until recently, this was the only timber truss bridge left on a main line railway. Fungal decay was discovered in the wood in 2001 necessitating a complete renovation. It is no longer entirely wood as concrete members have been introduced with new foundations, so that no load is carried on the wooden structure.

In the early 1890s, Murdoch was asked to be consulting engineer for the reconstruction of the old "Black Bridge" over the river Ness. With the engineer John Mackenzie, the Waterloo Bridge was constructed of iron trusses and opened in 1896.

Murdoch did take the odd working holiday! In April 1893, he was staying with Frances and Violet at Fortrose, then a favourite holiday place for Invernessians. He could see how the Black Isle line was progressing and had several meetings with John Ross while he was there. This line opened in February 1894.

Over in the west the Kyle extension was progressing despite severe blizzards in 1895. Lines were blocked and trains delayed. Cuttings filled up with snow. Murdoch's report to the directors in April said that the rock excavations were progressing well. The spoil was useful for the embankments where the track was near the sea. He said thirty-seven per cent of the excavation was complete. Seven bridges were under construction. There was good progress on the pier at Kyle in spite of gales and storms at sea. Seven hundred men were working on the job. The influx of all these people had an effect on the local communities. The papers were always reporting drunkenness and lewd behaviour, which did not please the God–fearing Free Church inhabitants. By the end of the summer, seventy-five per cent of the excavation was complete.

Whereas in the past pick and shovel were used for rock clearing, explosives now dislodged the extra hard rock of this part of Scotland. After explosions that were no doubt heard all over the area, the rock was cleared by hand.

At Erbusaig, then a fishing village just a few miles north of Kyle, the line is on a causeway or

The approach to Kyle of Lochalsh from the bridge above the railway. The whole area of track in view had to be cut out of solid rock.   *(Highland Railway Society/Roberts collection)*

The viaduct over the river Nairn south of Culloden Moor under construction with wooden scaffolding under the arches as illustrated in the Transactions of the Inverness Field Club Volume 5, page 185. The larger centre arch can be seen on the right.

embankment across the bay. The village is low lying with no flat land behind on which to build a railway. The villagers understood that there were to be three openings in the embankment for their boats to pass through but even after complaints to their Member of Parliament, Malcolm MacNeill, there was still only one opening. They felt that this problem would severely disrupt their boats and, of course, it blocked their beautiful view of Skye. There were many constraints in building this line brought about by its topography. Keeping to budget was difficult on what was then one of the most expensive railways per mile in Britain. To this day, there are problems with storms washing away sections, so it was probably thought extra openings were not a good idea, not to mention the extra cost.

In August 1897, the Inverness Field Club had an excursion to view the building of the Nairn viaduct at Culloden on the Aviemore to Inverness line. The Field Club, still in existence, is one of the prestigious organisations in Inverness so perhaps it was an indication of Murdoch's failing health that he delegated leading the excursion to his assistant for that section Mr D J Reid. The previous March Mr Reid addressed the Club on the "Geological Features of the Cuttings on the Inverness end of the Aviemore Line." This lecture and excursion give a valuable insight into the problems of constructing a railway line through wild and rugged country.

The Culloden Viaduct over the river Nairn and many of the other bridges are constructed of red sandstone, the underlying rock of the area. Two quarries supplied the stone; one was at the south

Leanach Quarry was one of the quarries from which stone for the viaduct was obtained, as illustrated in the Transactions of the Inverness Field Club Volume 5, page 261.

Daviot station, seen from the rear of a departing southbound train in 1960. This was the terminus station on section opened in July 1897 and the end of double track up the hill from Inverness.
(J L Stevenson)

end of the moor and the other about a mile west of the viaduct. The stone from each is identical. The viaduct is on a graceful curve with twenty-eight semicircular arches of fifty feet and an arch over the river of one hundred feet. The piers, apart from the span over the river, taper from six and a half feet thick at the base to five feet at the springline of the arches. It is the longest stone viaduct in Scotland.

The contractor ran a temporary railway from the quarries to carry the stone. On the north side of the viaduct bores showed that the rock was at a depth of four to five feet, so the piers were able to be on solid rock foundations. On the south side at the contact with the slope of the opposite bank, there was no rock at a similar depth. The surveyors went down fifteen feet and there was still no rock so the piers here rest on gravel and boulder clay with considerable amounts of concrete.

So great was this work that in July 1894 the contractors for the section from Daviot to just outside Inverness at Millburn, Mackay & Mackay, went bankrupt. A new contract with Charles Brand & Son in August meant that work could resume. To add to the complications, in September 1897 the directors decided to extend the double line from Culloden Moor as far as Daviot. That involved rebuilding some of the smaller bridges.

This coincided with the completion of the line to Kyle of Lochalsh. The Board of Trade inspection, by Major Sir Francis Marindin, took place on Thursday 28th October. Murdoch, William Roberts and Alexander Newlands, the resident engineer, accompanied him in the saloon carriage, along with Sir George MacPherson-Grant, then Chairman of the Highland Railway, and various other officials. Even then, it was realised that this railway was something

As well as the great viaducts on the direct line from Aviemore, many small bridges were required for roads and farm access. Typical is this bridge near Tomatin.
(Keith Fenwick)

The Station-master's house at Culloden where Murdoch spent his last days. It is now a private house.
(Anne-Mary Paterson)

special. A quarter of its ten and a half mile length is through deep cuttings of hard igneous rock. As the train wriggles its way along the coast, each open section presents a different scene of the coast stretching over the sea to Skye and northwards.

The line to Kyle was officially opened to the public on 2nd November 1897. There was the usual outing of the great and the good. A banquet was held at Strome Ferry on 2nd November. Sadly, Murdoch could not be present because of the state of his health. All agreed, "the railway would stand as an abiding memorial to the great ability and successful efforts of Murdoch Paterson and John Best."

The direct line from Aviemore to Inverness was also nearing completion and the Culloden Viaduct was rising spectacularly. Murdoch's health was deteriorating rapidly by the spring of 1898. He wished to see his dream reach fruition. In the early summer he decided to live in what was to be the stationmaster's house at Culloden, close to the viaduct, so that he could supervise the last minute details with the least effort to himself. We do not know whether Frances and Violet went too but one imagines that they and a servant would have stayed some of the time, to keep an eye on him and provide him with proper nourishment.

John Ross, the contractor, records in his diary for Wednesday, 8th June 1898 that he "went to Culloden Station to see Mr Paterson. Had a short talk with him. He is verey weak." However on the following Friday Murdoch met John Ross at Daviot Station. By Wednesday 20th July, he records that

Culloden Moor station in 1950, looking towards the viaduct.
(J L Stevenson)

Murdoch was very poorly.

With his strength ebbing away Murdoch knew that he would not live to see the opening of the Daviot to Inverness section. He realised that he did not even have the strength to walk across his beloved viaduct. He considered it his masterpiece and would have realised that it would stand for many years as a memorial to him but that he would never cross it on a train. As he did not wish to leave this world without crossing it for one last time, he asked if the men working on the finishing touches would put him on a trolley so that he could be pushed across. He arrived back at the stationmaster's house after this outing pleased that everything was in order and the line nearly ready for opening.

He died on Tuesday 9th August 1898 in the stationmaster's house, still very much in charge of the work. William Roberts was with him at the time and presumably Frances and Violet.

The funeral the following Saturday afternoon was from his home, Achanor. The *Inverness Courier* gave an account as follows, "Previous to the removal of the coffin, Dr Norman Macleod conducted a service in the house. The funeral was a very large one, and as the procession wended its way to Tomnahurich Cemetery, it was watched by large crowds. Along the route tokens of respect were evident, all the places of business being closed and the blinds drawn on the windows of dwelling houses. At the cemetery Dr Macleod conducted a short service."

Among the pall bearers at the burial were Andrew Paterson, a nephew, established as a civil engineer in Brazil, John Paterson, my grandfather, and William Roberts, his faithful and esteemed assistant. Among the mourners as well as directors and heads of department of the Highland Railway were many of his workers and citizens of Inverness. Obviously, he was held in very high esteem.

And so ended a life full of action; a life which was usefully spent by a well liked man, and which changed the face of the Highlands forever. This is a story that begins and ends at Culloden.

Murdoch getting ready to be pushed across the viaduct not long before he died.

(Drawing by Olivia Brotheridge)

EPILOGUE

Janet, William's elder daughter, remained unmarried. Margaret, married to John Arres-Mather, had two sons, William and James, and four daughters, Janet, Rachel, Margaret and Roberta. William and Rachel, who both died young, were unmarried. Margaret married Dr Mackay, a well-known medical practitioner in Inverness. Roberta married William Baxter and they lived at Clonburn, Resaurie, Inverness. Neither Margaret nor Roberta had any children. James, who managed the estates in Ireland, died of pneumonia in 1920. Janet continued to live at Wester Delnies. As a small child, I used to spend Easter holidays there with my Aunt Margaret, my father's sister.

After Murdoch's older daughter, Elizabeth, emigrated with William Murray to Australia, she had two daughters, Elena Jane in 1878 and Violet Elizabeth in 1886. Their descendants and that of the older son, Murdoch, now live in New Zealand. Violet, Murdoch and Frances' daughter, married Frederick Dutton, a schoolmaster in Essex. Frances went to live with them. Violet had three daughters, none of whom married. They lived in Seaford, Sussex until their deaths.

William and Murdoch were the first members of the Paterson family to become professional civil engineers. They had a direct line back to the first president of the Institution of Civil Engineers, Thomas Telford, through Joseph Mitchell, and started a new dynasty of civil engineers.

John and Mary Paterson and their sons outside Yewbank, Beauly, accompanied by Spot, the dog. John and Mary stand behind their three sons. William is the smallest boy, *(Anne-Mary Paterson colln.)*

William Paterson (1896-1964), my father and a grandnephew of William and Murdoch lived with his family in Beauly, where his father, John was an ironmonger and seed merchant. In 1913 William was taken on as an apprentice civil engineer on the Highland Railway by William Roberts, Murdoch's assistant and then successor, just before he retired.

I think William would have liked to go to university to study civil engineering, but the First World War was looming and he knew that his brothers, Alastair and Donald who were in the territorials, would be called to the front. In any case, he was only seventeen so he probably thought he would see how he liked the job. Both brothers went to the war and were killed at the Battle of Festubert. My grandmother, Mary, when she heard that Alastair had died of wounds, took a heart attack in London on the way to visit him in hospital near Rouen. My grandfather took ill soon after and died in 1916. Being on the railway, my father was in protected employment, so after the war there was no question of his leaving home. Anyway, by this time his apprenticeship was well on its way.

William Paterson, my father. He was another William called after his granduncle.

(Anne-Mary Paterson colln.)

It must have been hard learning from a correspondence course amid all this turmoil. Alexander Newlands, Roberts' successor, gave him a lot of help and of course he was getting practical railway experience. Alexander Newlands came from Findochty. Like William Roberts, he had trained at Gordon & MacBey, who were surveyors and engineers in Elgin, before joining the Highland Railway.

William's first experience of railway disasters was on a summer day, 18th June 1914, when there was a cloudburst in the hills near Carr Bridge. The Baddengorm burn, up till then an insignificant trickle, became a wall of water nearly twenty feet high which undermined the railway bridge. Sadly, a train from Perth to Inverness had just left Carr Bridge Station at 3.25 p.m. and the bridge collapsed under it, so creating a gap of about fifty feet in the embankment and dislodging some one hundred and fifty feet of track The three middle carriages were washed away and five passengers were drowned. All the engineering staff were involved in the rebuilding, which was carried out expeditiously in three weeks.

When the First World War broke out in August 1914 the Highland Railway, although previously thought of as being in a "backwater," took on national significance. It became the main supply route for the British Navy bases at Invergordon and Scapa Flow in Orkney. There were many extra trains for troops, munitions and supplies. New sidings were needed. In the Highland Council Archives a diary by an unknown junior engineer records William surveying for additional sidings at Invergordon. Later he was doing the same for a wood carting system at Orbliston on the Aberdeen line south of Elgin.

In 1915 and 1916, every bridge was surveyed because of the amount of traffic they carried. In 1915, a heavier locomotive called the "River" Class 4-6-0s arrived for service. The civil engineering department spent a whole weekend on overtime, working out the stresses on the bridges brought about by the extra weight of the engines. The Highland Railway civil engineer then rejected the "River" Class because of this.

During and after the war my Aunt Margaret tried to carry on my grandfather's business, in which Alastair was also involved. Donald, the other brother, also killed, was training to be an architect. Even with the help of my grandfather's brother, also William, who was in a similar line in Invergordon, the family had so many difficulties that the business folded.

William went to London to sit his final exam. In his hotel, the night before, he suddenly wondered if there would be a question on tunnelling of which he had had little practical experience as there are only three short ones on the Highland Railway. He looked this up in his books and memorised the methods. Sure enough, there was a question, so he was able to answer it with confidence.

By 1923 when the Highland Railway became part of the London Midland & Scottish Railway, usually referred to as the LMS, William was a fully-qualified civil engineer, enjoying his work on the railway lines created by his great uncles. However, there were new ways to learn after amalgamation. I think that this was the part of his career that he enjoyed most. In later years, when we travelled on the train or in the family car between Glasgow and Beauly, he used to regale us with tales of those days and I got the impression that, like Murdoch, he knew most of the railway staff and their families. He was very involved with the game of shinty, an old Highland team game, sometimes rather unkindly described as hockey without rules. When we went anywhere in the Highlands, there was always someone who would come to speak to him as though he was a long lost friend. Being six foot four inches tall, he did stand out in a crowd!

On 8th July 1923, there was another cloudburst in the Carr Bridge area. It washed away the railway and road bridges over the Bogbain burn. Mercifully, no trains were on the line so no lives were lost. William was in charge of the repairs and his earlier experiences in the area must have been of assistance. The railway was closed longer than before, until 31st August. I remember him saying he was away from home for several weeks.

With the amalgamation, there were more career opportunities for staff. In 1925, Alexander Newlands was promoted to Divisional Civil Engineer for the former London & North Western system at Crewe. Archie McMurdo, his assistant, succeeded him. Archie was a kindly man who was married to a local girl, Christina Mackenzie. In 1929, Archie moved to London and William became district engineer.

He was still living in the old Beauly family home, Yewbank, Ferry Road, with his mother, who having had a heart attack required careful attention from his sister, Margaret. In the 1920s a young doctor, Roderick Mackay came to Beauly as an assistant to one of the local doctors, Dr Thomas MacDonald. He and my father struck up a close friendship. My father went out with him on many calls, especially at night and, of course, the work on the railway involved night calls when there was an incident. He got used to disturbed nights and could sleep almost anywhere.

When not at work he enjoyed shooting, fishing and golf but his great love was still shinty. Brothers Alastair and Donald had played for the Beauly team and in 1913, under Alastair's captainship, they had won the Camanachd Cup, the supreme award. In 1923 William became secretary of the Camanachd Association, the ruling body for shinty, and in 1937 was elected President. He spent many winter afternoons on draughty fields watching matches.

In spite of her delicacy, my grandmother survived until May 1935. In 1936, William met my Mother, appropriately, at Euston Station when they were both arriving for the overnight sleeper to Inverness. Although my mother did not live in Beauly, her parents came from the place. She had spent many of her holidays there and would call on my Grandmother Paterson. They married in London in December 1936.

The 1930s was a period of cost cutting for the LMS, an example being the introduction of motorised trolleys so that permanent way gangs could cover longer sections. When war broke out in 1939, the Highland lines had to be geared up once again to take increased traffic, just as had been done during World War I, when William joined the Highland Railway.

However, his preparations were interrupted because in 1940 he was appointed district engineer for the Glasgow Central District. From the time of Joseph Mitchell there had been a direct link of engineers at Inverness on the Highland line, and this was now broken. The move to Glasgow presented many new challenges. Initially he stayed in St Enoch Station Hotel and travelled to Beauly when he could at weekends. Frequently the hotel was in darkness during and after bombing raids and the guests had to find their way about with candles! Eventually he and my mother found a nice house near Eastwood Toll in Giffnock, a suburb to the south west of Glasgow. The house was a seven-minute walk to Williamwood Station for commuting to work.

Night work was common when there were incidents. There was fire watching at the office and air raid patrol work when he was at home; but there was always a summer break in Beauly, still his great love.

Peace came at last but not to the railway. It was worn out with the traffic it had carried and in 1948 it was nationalised by the government. Peace also meant that shinty could resume and William was much involved in starting it up. In April 1947, I had my first visit to Oban for the Camanachd Final between Newtonmore and Lochfyneside. There was great excitement. Unfortunately, the afternoon turned out very wet but that did not seem to quell the enthusiasm. Newtonmore won four goals to nil.

As in 1923, there were now new ways to learn in British Railways. There were frustrations from people above who were inexperienced in the workings of a railway. One of the more unusual tasks given to the District Engineer was responsibility for the western end of the Forth & Clyde Canal. I think it must have been in rather a dilapidated state because it appeared to need a lot of attention. I often accompanied my Father on a Sunday afternoon to look at a job on some part of it. With the formation of British Waterways, he handed the task over to them.

In 1954, he became assistant chief civil engineer for Scotland, in charge of the civil engineering for the electrification of the Glasgow suburban lines on the 25kV AC system, with 6.25kV in the central area. It may seem strange that civil engineering was involved in electrification. The clearance needed for the high voltage overhead wires for the electrification meant that greater height was needed. One hundred and sixty five bridges were affected. Ninety-five had to be rebuilt, track lowered in thirty-eight and thirty-two raised. In some cases temporary Bailey Bridges had to be erected to allow road traffic to continue.

Paterson Family house near Eastwood Toll, Giffnock, Glasgow in the 1950s. The author stands on the left beside her mother in the centre and a family friend. (Anne-Mary Paterson colln)

A Glasgow Blue Train approaches Maxwell Park on the first day of service in 1962. The bridge behind has been raised to give clearance for the overhead electric wires. The electric units were considered very advanced for their day. Although a development of an LMS design pioneered over 20 years before, the units were thoroughly up to date thanks to the involvement of the BTC Design Panel. (James Stevenson)

The Airdrie to Helensburgh line on the north side of the Clyde had a series of long tunnels under Glasgow city centre leading to Queen Street Low Level Station. Because of the need for clearance for the wires in the tunnels, designed in the nineteenth century for steam traffic, all had to have their track lowered but of course with the least inconvenience to the travelling public. As George Blake wrote in *Glasgow Electric* "It was in fact the virtual demolition of an obsolescent system and the creation of a new one over its ruins." It is notable that the electrification project was completed without any prolonged suspension of passenger services such as would happen today.

Stations were redesigned. The biggest alterations were at Glasgow Queen Street, a grim smoky relic of steam days, where the new electrified lines passed through its low-level station. This was completely rebuilt much to the delight of its users.

The team of engineers, civil, mechanical and signalling, were all based together in Electrification House, a building on Argyll Street under St Enoch Station. This meant that everyone involved had easy access to one another. The first lines in Britain to be electrified with mixed AC voltage were out of Liverpool Street in London so there were many visits south to view that work.

The Airdrie to Helensburgh section opened on Monday, 7th November 1960. On the Sunday, there were trial runs. I accompanied my parents on a ride from Queen Street Low Level to Helensburgh and back. I remember that there was a glass partition behind the driver's cab so there was a wonderful view as the train sped alongside the Firth of Clyde.

There were, of course, the inevitable delays during the opening period. The trains had automatic sliding doors. Passengers unaccustomed to this innovation were frightened they would be trapped in a door as the train set off! The electric trains also had to be withdrawn for ten months due to problems with their switchgear. Electrification of the lines on the south side of the Clyde was completed in 1962.

I think my father wanted to take early retirement to Beauly but he decided to stay on to see the work for the "blue trains", as they were called, completed. This colour went back to the days of the Caledonian Railway locomotives.

Towards the end of this period, he was busy planning the alterations to the house in Beauly. He retired in September 1961 but, sadly, he was only to enjoy a short retirement there. He died in July 1964.

Andrew Paterson (b1847) was a nephew of Murdoch and William and a brother of my grandfather. He practised civil engineering in Brazil. A letter to my grandfather, John Paterson, suggests that he had something to do with a tunnel in Rio de Janeiro. In the early years of the twentieth century, the city began to expand to the south and west. To improve communications a tunnel was built under the mountains to the neighbourhood now known as Copacabana. His papers were destroyed in the London blitz during the Second World War so we do not know for certain if he had anything to do with this tunnel. He must have been successful in his work, as he also owned a house in Shepperton on the river Thames. My father and my Aunt Margaret used to spend holidays there.

Donald (Do-Do) Paterson (1882-1938) was a first cousin of my father. Donald's father was the factor for estates in South Uist. He was educated at Inverness Royal Academy and then apprenticed to James Barron. After completing this, he worked at Dover Docks. He then went to Singapore and Malaya where he was involved in the building and design of the Johore Causeway that crosses from Singapore to Malaya. The causeway, constructed of rubble and completed in June 1924, is wide enough to carry a roadway and a double track railway. He later went to work at Beira in East Africa. He died in May 1938 aged 56.

Kenneth Murdoch Paterson (b1894) was a brother of Do-Do and also a civil engineer but no records seem to be available of his career.

Duncan Kennedy's great grandmother Isabella was a sister of William and Murdoch's father, Donald, the farmer at Dell of Inshes. Duncan started his civil engineering career on the Connel to Ballachulish Railway, a branch of the railway from Glasgow to Oban. After he retired he wrote an interesting book *The Life and Death of a Highland Railway* on his experiences during its construction. In it, he says his mother sometimes spoke of Murdoch, which gave him the idea of civil engineering. Duncan's father had a small farm near to where the railway was to pass. This gave him his first chance to learn his trade with the contractors. He later worked on the Aswan Dam in Egypt, the Jacques Cartier Bridge in Canada and Takoradi Container Docks in Ghana. When he was engaged on the latter, he was unable to find a contractor so he organised the construction himself using native labour.

When he returned to Britain, he was in charge of the Inverness office of Sir William Halcrow & Partners supervising the construction of the many hydroelectric schemes in which they were involved including the Glen Affric and Morriston schemes. He used to visit us when we were on holiday in Beauly.

After he retired, as well as writing the book already mentioned, even at eighty he used to travel the world to visit and report to Halcrows on the condition of jobs he had worked on. He died in Beckenham, Kent in July 1974.

Murdoch MacDonald (later Sir Murdoch MacDonald, M.P.) was a native of Inverness. From 1886 to 1889, he served an apprenticeship under Murdoch Paterson. He was then resident engineer on the construction of the Black Isle Branch. Being a man of some enterprise, he was also involved in schemes for a water supply to Fortrose, Rosemarkie and Avoch. He may have surveyed the Garve to Ullapool line. Other Highland railway projects he was involved in include doubling parts of the line from Stanley to Aviemore and the extension to Kyle of Lochalsh. Here he met his wife, Margaret Munro, daughter of the Kyle postmaster.

In 1898, he went to Egypt to work for the Egyptian Government as assistant to Sir Maurice Fitzmorris on the construction of the Aswan Dam. He was then resident engineer on the dam and was so successful with this that he became Director General of Reservoirs. During the First World War, he served in the Royal Engineers and rose to the rank of colonel. He twice won the Telford Medal, awarded by the Institution of Civil Engineers, for his work on the Nile.

He left Egypt in 1922 to found his own consulting civil engineering company, first as MacDonald & MacCorquodale, then as Sir Murdoch Macdonald & Partners. Alexander MacCorquodale was a former colleague from Inverness who was one of several Highland Railway civil engineers and had followed Macdonald to Egypt. In the 1920s and 1930s Murdoch MacDonald was still involved with Egypt, in heightening the Aswan Dam and other works. In Britain, the company designed the Great Ouse Flood Protection Scheme. When the hydroelectric schemes started in the North of Scotland, he was a member of the panel of consulting engineers to the North of Scotland Hydroelectric Board.

He was elected president of the Institution of Civil Engineers in 1932. He was the Liberal and then National Liberal Member of Parliament for Inverness from 1922 until 1950. He died in Nairn in 1956.

His admiration for Murdoch continued throughout his life. He spoke of Murdoch in glowing terms when my father once introduced me to him. I think that he greatly enjoyed his time on the Highland Railway. Murdoch Paterson was from time to time involved in other engineering work on the sidelines especially in his early days, so he probably turned a blind eye to the other Murdoch's extra curricular activities. When he was made a freeman of Inverness in 1930 he said that he had learnt civil engineering "at the feet of that first-class engineer and kindliest of men, the late Murdoch Paterson."

His company is now part of Mott MacDonald, an engineering and management consultancy. Their recent work on Scottish railways has included the refurbishment of some of the old Highland Railway stations, so the lineage stretching down from Telford, Mitchell, Paterson and MacDonald continues in the Highlands into the twenty-first century.

BIBLIOGRAPHY

Anderson Isabel Harriet   Inverness before Railways; A & W Mackenzie 1885
Blake George   Glasgow Electric; British Railways, Scotland 1960
Cameron A D   The Caledonian Canal; Birlinn 2005
Campbell John Edgar   The Iron Track through the Highlands; Highland News about 1923
Dowds T J   The Forth and Clyde Canal; Tuckwell Press 2003
Ford Christopher R   Dunkeld, Telford's Finest Highland Bridge; Perth & Kinross Libraries 2004
Fraser John   Reminiscences of Inverness, Its People & Places; Charles Leakey 1983
Gifford John   The Buildings of Scotland, Highlands and Islands; Penguin Books 1992
Haldane A R B   New Ways through the Glens; Nelson 1962
Hunter D L G   The Highland Railway in Retrospect; Moorfoot Publishing 1998
Kennedy Duncan   The Birth and Death of a Highland Railway; John Murray 1971
Mackay T   The Life of Sir John Fowler; John Murray 1900
Martin Don   The Monkland & Kirkintilloch and Associated Railways; Strathkelvin Libraries & Museums 1995
May Trevor   The Victorian Railway Worker; Shire Publications 2003
McConnell David   Rails to Wick & Thurso; Dornoch Press
McConnell David   Rails to Kyle of Lochalsh; Oakwood Press 1997
Mitchell Joseph   Reminiscences of My Life in the Highlands (1884) Vols 1 & 2; David & Charles 1971
Nelson Gillian   Highland Bridges; Aberdeen University Press 1990
O'Dell A C & Walton Kenneth   The Highlands & Islands of Scotland; Nelson 1962
Page Colin B   The Episcopal Church in Ross-shire in the 18th & 19th Centuries
Paterson M Mackenzie   Other Days, The Story of a Black Isle Family
Paxton Roland & Shipway Jim   Civil Engineering Heritage Scotland Highlands and Islands; Thomas Telford Ltd 2007
Pearson Michael   Iron Road to Whisky Country; Wayzgoose 2002
Pearson Michael   Iron Road to the Highlands; Wayzgoose 2002
Pearson Michael   Iron Roads to the Far North & Kyle; Wayzgoose 2003
Rolt L T C   Victorian Engineering; Allen Lane 1970
Ross David   The Highland Railway; Tempus Publishing 2005, second edition Stenlake Publishing 2010.
Sedgwick Sheila   The Legion of the Lost, The Story of Glen Muick, Royal Deeside; Private Publication 1999
Simmons Jack   The Victorian Railway; Thames & Hudson 1991
Sinclair Neil T   Highland Railway: People and Places; Breedon Books 2005
Sinclair Neil T   The Highland Main Line; Atlantic Publishers 1998
Smout T C   A Century of the Scottish People 1830 - 1950; Collins 1986
Sutherland, Elizabeth   A New Age, Episcopalians in Ross 1780 – 1850
Thomas John   The Skye Railway; David St John Thomas 1977
Thomas John   A Regional History of the Railways of Great Britain Vol 6, Lowlands and the Borders; David & Charles 1971
Thomas John, Turnock David   A Regional History of the Railways of Great Britain Vol 15, North of Scotland; David & Charles 1989
Vallance H A   Great North of Scotland Railway; David St John Thomas 1989
Vallance H A   The History of the Highland Railway; Arthur H Stockwell 1938
Various Inverness Newspapers   Inverness Courier, Highland News, Weekly News, Northern Chronicle, North Star

INDEX

THE HIGHLAND RAILWAY SOCIETY

The Highland Railway Society caters for all those interested in the varied aspects of the railway, including its predecessors and its successors to the present day.

An illustrated quarterly Journal is distributed to members and contains a wide variety of articles and information. Members queries are a regular feature and details of new books, videos and models of interest are reported. The Society's publications include a series of books commemorating the 150th anniversaries of the opening of various sections of the system.

Meetings are held regularly in both Scotland and England. An annual gathering is held each September and includes a full day of talks, films, etc., as well as an opportunity to meet fellow members.

The Society has Library, Photographic and Drawing collections which are available to members. Copies of drawings are available for purchase. Modellers are well catered for. Complete kits are produced in limited runs. Specially commissioned modelling components such as axle boxes, buffers and springs are available, plus a comprehensive set of transfers to enable any Highland loco to be named.

Membership details can be found on the Society's website at www.hrsoc.org.uk.